with girders and glass and concrete. Cincinnati and Chattanooga breed their own busy accomplishment, their own smog.

More and more, as we explore ranges and waters and whistling freeways, we observe the ten Hamiltons (in New York, Ohio, Texas, Kansas, Nebraska, Iowa, Indiana, Illinois, Florida, Tennessee) as an entity. They melt into a unit native to American civilization.

The very name Hamilton *has a bell sound about it. . .*

Herein are contained shreds of history, reportage, personal anecdote, and that fiction which often becomes a more prevailing fact than fact itself.

Here are lives and landscapes which could not prosper or even exist in another Country.

A single rule has been dominant: every

picture represents some portion of Hamilton County; and every scrap of prose relates to creatures dwelling therein.

Dog or cat, infant or patriarch, meadow or slum . . . these are our sincere presentation of a far-flung region which we cherish.

Let us all go traveling together through

Hamilton County

The Macmillan Company

The Macmillan Company
866 Third Avenue, New York, N.Y. 10022
Collier-Macmillan Canada Ltd., Toronto, Ontario

Library of Congress Catalog Card Number: 70-101724

FIRST PRINTING

Book designed by Joan Stoliar
All reproductions from prints by Vincent Tcholak

Printed in the United States of America

This book is the combined effort of author and photographer, a father and his son.

Also a third generation is apparent. The author thanks his grandson, Tom Shroder, for casting a little light upon teen-age scenery so difficult for an elder to identify or discuss.

Only a few attempts have been made, either by the man with a pencil or the man with a camera, to tailor captions to the size of illustrations, or to embroider a tale with embellished photography.

Contents

to Ruth

Long Way... So Far

*T*he ridges make you think of Indians, especially during autumn days. You smell dry grass, and guess at how the air might have smelled when only harsh and primitive herbage was growing here . . . and none in sandy places in between.

You think of Indians swarming up over a hill. Suddenly in frightened imagery you look over and see them with their feathers and horseflesh, and human skins shining where they're bared and painted.

You are overwhelmed by spotted horses especially, because those seem particularly Indian: paint ponies, white folks called them, or *pintos*. And sun is gleaming on weapons the Indians carry, and you wonder whether they've seen you as you have seen them, and what they're going to do about it.

Sky is streaked, but light shafts brilliantly through the sheets of cloud, or between them, for a time . . . darker thicker cloud comes to blot the sun.

They varied, the natives did, in all sections of Hamilton County. In New York State there were Iroquois and Mohawk to be considered. Down along the Tennessee River— That was the land of the Cherokee. And, what with various related Shawnee in Indiana and Ohio, and Sauk and Fox in Illinois; and in Texas the Comanche; and the Arapaho and Kiowa, say, in

Kansas— In Iowa and Nebraska you think about the Sioux—in Nebraska especially. Their name for themselves was *Dakota*.

Hamilton County shoves its wedge shape against the Platte River. Along that same Platte the early wagon trails stretched west.

Let me tell about Grandpa and Grandma Bone traveling on one of those tortuous wagon roads.

The Seventh Iowa Cavalry had to be spread thinly, but in the end General Sully and other commanders gave the Seventh a very good bill of health. The regiment was parceled out, all the way from Fort Kearney to Fort Cottonwood to Fort McPherson — Away out to Fort Laramie, and down to Julesburg in Colorado Territory . . . they campaigned in Kansas too, and in what's now South Dakota. One regiment: they were all over the place. Maybe two companies at one post, three at another, two at the next, with hundreds of miles to be patrolled constantly, in between. It was the only way to keep the Cheyenne and Dakota (by that I mean the Sioux) in check. But with so few troopers to put in an appearance at the proper moment— Or before a fatal moment occurred— Well. Often the cavalry didn't get there in time.

When a private soldier was wounded—or "tooken sick," as they used to say—out on the frontier, it was just too bad. But in the case of an officer, the commander might write to his family back in the States, and ask if they wished to send someone to nurse him. Otherwise his fate was pretty well sealed. The soldiers themselves didn't have much time to devote to nursing.

Once, for instance, Company F was ordered to ride here, there, everywhere, between July 19th and August 24th, 1864. They added up a total distance of nine hundred and sixty-six miles. The horses were seldom in good shape, so that made it all the more remarkable.

Today you can journey nine hundred and sixty-six miles by commercial jet in a couple of hours, or in considerably less time in a military aircraft . . . people do that constantly, and leave those fluffy strips across the sky.

Wires hum their invocation and threnody, they sing of the long ago.

You halt to listen . . . stand or sit alone, and listen with all your ears. Often enough the wires will talk to you, high wires suspended between their poles.

Sometimes even the fence wires sing.

Like the strings of an instrument, with wind instead of fingers touching them delicately.

Sometimes there are even song whispers in dry tough weeds which stand hard and thin and bereft of green juices, waiting for death beneath the snows, waiting for warmer decay in a springtime far beyond.

Weeds and wires moan of Indians. Sometimes you can very nearly hear the Indian drums, threatening, percussive.

Oh, they didn't beat drums when they rubbed on their green and white and yellow paint, when they were bound to slay the whites who drove steadily forward to occupy the Indians' sacred lands. They did their drumming and singing before they started out. But the war song seemed to go with them.

It clings to the texture of long empty ridges.

Even now, even now.

The wires echo it.

I-ya! Ma-ni ni-yan wa. . . .

Wires and weeds in this our county.

Grandpa Bone was first lieutenant of Company G. It was fortunate that he was an officer. Someone expended the time and energy to write a letter to Joseph Bone's wife, back in the States, and ask her if there was somebody who could come out to Nebraska Territory and nurse the sick lieutenant.

Yes, there was somebody. She herself would go.

No one of the children was big enough or able enough—except maybe Son Jo, and Jo had already run away to the war. So the taller children must look after the smaller ones.

Grandma Bone worked fiercely at packing, giving instructions, trying to warn and encourage and adjure, all in the same breath. Fate did not smile upon her preparation. She had an ulcerated tooth. It was difficult to decide about what gowns to take along, and to remember what to tell the elder girls about looking after Baby Eva. . . .

In the dusk she called two of the nine children to her side and said, "Esther, you hold this looking-glass, so. Molly, you hold the lamp . . . closer, on this side. So's I can see."

She took a steel knitting needle and heated it in the flame of the lamp; then, watching carefully in the mirror, and forcing her lip aside with a finger of her other hand, she slowly drilled the red-hot knitting needle into the root of her sore tooth, to burn out the nerve.

See? With the nerve burned out and dead, after a while the swelling would go down. And anyway— Well, after that pain from the red-hot steel sliding through gum and tissue and into the very root socket— There wouldn't be any more pain, you understand. That is, not the same pain. It would just be sore, kind of. For a while.

. . . She rocked along in a stagecoach to Omaha, and then out along the Platte in other stages; then bounced and shook in Army wagons from one station to the next. No Indians attacked the wagons because there were too many soldiers along. At last Grandma Bone reached Fort Cottonwood where her husband lay, and she nursed him until he grew stronger.

Not strong enough to resume active campaigning. No, Joseph Bone was through as a soldier. He could go home and resign his commission; that is, if he was able to stand the journey. He was only thirty-four years old, and had been tough as nails to begin with, but those sore fever-ridden weeks took quite a toll. If he made the journey, he'd do it lying down.

They fetched out one of those high-wheeled wagons. It was built away up off the ground with oversized wheels to cope with thick sand which clogged the trail in many places. They set out, with the sick man stretched on a litter in the back of the wagon, and his wife beside him, and a teamster holding the reins of a four-mule team. There was precious little forage for animals on those ridges along the Platte. They had to carry fodder: big sacks piled up in the wagon. Six troopers rode their horses ahead and alongside.

They were two days east of the fort, and it was afternoon, and sun was brilliant in the sky behind them. They came up over a summit and looked ahead.

Indians.

The warriors were massed on a hill to the northeast, and their feathers shone.

You look over and see them . . . skins shining where they're bared and painted . . . milling around and waiting.

A field glass was passed from hand to hand, and a certain cold sickness took hold of the soldiers' hearts. And the woman's.

(It must have been so. I have never seen a band of hostile Indians waiting on a hill ahead . . . but mightn't it be something like watching enemy fighters emerging from their hiding places behind piled-up cumulus, and heading toward you, with leading edges of their wings alight with guns? Or like approaching a city you've got to attack, and seeing the sky above that target solidly forested by bulbous stunted Christmas trees of flak; and thinking, "This is it. We've *had* it. I wish we were home in *bed.*")

One of the troopers pushed his horse to the back of the wagon and cried, "Lieutenant Bone, I been along this here road a lot of times. There's an old soddy—" A sod dugout: the first hovel which newcomers usually built. "It's back to the south on that next hill. If we can get there before the Indians get to us, maybe we can hold em off. A while, anyways."

The lieutenant whispered, "Yes. Go ahead," and away they went at full career, the wagon jerking from hummock to hummock, bounding over piles of earth above the holes the rodents dug, rocking up out of a dry watercourse, following whatever path suggested itself as wisest from the wagoner's standpoint . . . cavalrymen galloping on their sorry horses. . . .

Well, they reached the sod dugout. Why the Indians hadn't raced to attack them they couldn't understand. They were much closer now . . . instead of fleeing from the Indians, they'd had to advance toward them. The soddy wasn't much—its roof had caved in—but those walls were thick, they would stop arrows, maybe even stop rifle bullets.

Men lifted Grandpa Bone out of the wagon and put him at the back of the dugout, with his wife; and then the troopers piled up the fodder sacks in the apertures, and put their carbines across them. They began to count out cartridges.

Assuredly you can hear those wires stretching over the rolling prairie, over hills and ridges . . . wires sagging between poles or tight between them . . . fence wires telling the tale. They hum and say, "Ah yes. In springtime, the wild roses— You should come in the spring!"

Wires tell us, "Once the buffalo were here, way over yonder, right up on that third rise. There's an old wallow: a big hole the buffalo made, where they used to lie down and rub themselves in the dry loose dirt. First one would do it, then another, then a lot more, and pretty soon there'd be a great big wide hole dug out."

. . . Chunks of dark hair mingled with the dirt. And animals would die in a wallow sometimes, and there'd be skulls and bones. Then, eventually, when there were no more buffalo to come and disturb the soil, grasses started to grow again. But the shape of the wallow would be there still, and is there today, and you can go and find it.

Let us sing of buffalo and of Dakota, or Cheyenne or Pawnee. So many Indians on their ponies.

Waiting.

Flicker of movement in the eastern valley, some portion of the scenery detaching itself, crawling around a corner and coming on west. It was a wagon with a torn canvas cover, and there came another behind . . . more wagons, ox-drawn . . . five in all. (The soldiers seldom called them emigrant trains. They spoke of "movers.")

Ah, land waiting, somewhere beyond. Claims which families could prove up . . . or were there gold nuggets to be had for the digging, out on the Pacific Coast?

. . . Sad news, sad news. Those wagons weren't going anywhere, no farther than this. They were what the Indians had been waiting for, and already wild riders were pouring pell-mell down off that ridge where they'd crowded in ambush. Feathers, paint, weapon-glint, ponies . . . yells. The hill was boiling over.

"Reckon there's a hundred—"

"Pshaw. Hundred and fifty."

"More like *two* hundred."

The scene was hideously close at hand when one watched it through the glass. But it could be observed with the naked eye, and so Grandma Bone saw it. She had it burned into her memory, the way that savage steel penetrated the tissues of her jaw. Now an imaginary red-hot needle of fright and agony went branding its way into her brain.

She would never forget.

The wagons had started to corral in a defensive ring, but there wasn't time to complete the maneuver before the Indians struck. It was the fatal counter-clockwise circle so common to warfare on plains and deserts of the West: the whirling file of warriors riding round and round in ghastly carousel. The handful of movers fought back, they did their best.

The watching little squad of troopers mumbled among themselves.

"Soon as they get through with *them*, they'll come up here and finish us off."

"Yep. We'll just be frosting on the cake."

"Well, I aim to get me a few before they take *my* hair."

There was grim satisfaction in seeing several of the attackers tumble from their horses, but the fight didn't last long. It couldn't. Soon the Indians had stopped their merry-go-round careering, and were darting in among the wagons. Smoke began to go up.

A corporal who held the field glasses at the moment reported that some women were being carried off . . . women, of course. Plains Indians held the notion that the sex act should be mingled with the act of war. That made it rough going for any females they encountered.

I know an old Dakota war song, and sometimes chant it— at least to myself, when wishing to discomfit enemies. There is a reiteration, *Ho! Ha! He! Chay!* and those words are concerned with sex. It is easy to believe that Grandma Bone covered her face with her hands when it was reported that women were being seized.

. . . What was this? The Indians— Going away?

They streamed up over hills to the north, leaving burning wagons behind them, and bodies strewn about. They lugged along their own dead and wounded too.

Going *away?*

"It's a trick."

"Sure it's a trick. They'll be back."

"They *couldn't* have missed seeing us!"

"They know we're here. . . ."

"Couldn't have missed!"

But they had missed. There was that business about the sun being bright in western sky . . . the little party at the ruined sod-house had gone unreported, unwitnessed. Brilliant sunlight would have been in the Indians' eyes if they'd gazed in that direction. They'd been watching the puny caravan approaching from the east.

Those five wagons were at the end of the road. So were the dead who lay among the embers.

Folks in the soddy waited a long time. No Indians. At last, with caution, they loaded Lieutenant Bone back into the wagon. A couple of courageous individuals (they do seem especially brave, as we think of them now) rode ahead to scout—as an advance guard, as a possible preliminary sacrifice. But— No Indians.

They signaled for the others to come down.

Wagons were still smoldering. Boxes and barrels and trunks had been broken open, food was strewn about; horses and cattle lay slaughtered.

And the people—ah, the people. . . .

Several small children with mangled heads, their brains knocked out. Four dead women. Then—the men. They'd all been scalped.

Grandma Bone said, "We must bury em."

"Easiest way, ma'am, is to dig a long trench. Then just put em in it, in a row, side by side."

They wanted to be well out of there before dark. The Indians might have left scouts in the neighborhood . . . there was no telling. Dig the shallow grave, cover up the bodies, get out of there as rapidly as possible.

In that dry air, rigor mortis had already set in, the corpses were stiffening. One man was pierced by an arrow, and he'd grabbed hold of the shaft, perhaps trying to pull it out of his chest. His arm was rigid. It was difficult to force the arm down against the congealed body. The soldiers broke the arrow off, in order to bury that man.

Slowly, Grandma Bone picked up the arrow. . . .

They covered the long trench. There wasn't anything they could do about burying horses and cattle. Actually the Indians had sliced tenderloins out of the cattle; they usually did that, and the tongues as well. Not because those cattle had spoken with the tongues of cattle and angels, and the Indians didn't want them to use their tongues in the next world. Nay. (That's the reason they'd build a fire between a dead man's legs and burn off— So he couldn't procreate in Paradise, you see.) The Indians took the cattle tongues because they liked to eat cattle tongues.

A few days later a patrol from the First Nebraska Territorial Infantry (Mounted) came past, and discovered the wreckage and that common grave. They uncovered the grave and count-ed the bodies. Eighteen, I was always told by my grandmother.

"Nineteen," said old Michael James Dooley when I talked with him, sixty-six years after the massacre.

He said he was only fifteen years old at the time.

· "Nineteen bodies," he insisted. I wasn't about to argue the point with him, because he was there and I wasn't.

"Even being a young boy, way I was, I felt very devout. It didn't seem right to me not to have that grave marked in proper fashion. I says to our commander, 'Captain, sir, don't you think we ought to put up a cross, whilst we're camped nearby, tonight?' The captain, he laughed and he says, 'Boy, if you can find enough wood in this country to make a cross, you got my permission to put one up.' That night I stole two boards out of the sutler's wagon, and I hid em; and then, after the sutler had drove on with some of our troops next morning, I hung back and fastened that cross together, and stuck it up on the grave."

When I was a boy I used to ask my grandmother what had become of the arrow, the one broken off so that they might bury the man. . . .

"I don't know. It was around, somewhere in the family . . . then it disappeared. I suppose that children got to playing with it . . . anyway it's gone. We haven't seen it in years."

One day, in middle age, I was putting away some family treasures, and came across a little tube-shaped box. Just a plain tube—looked like a section of thick broomstick—but you could unscrew the top end, and take it off, and it was hollow inside. That box had been constructed especially for the purpose of containing steel knitting needles. I dumped the needles out and examined them. One was scorched and purpled by flame; the discoloration showed plainly. I put the needles back into the tube, and it's stowed away in our attic now.

. . . Maybe some kid had been toasting marshmallows with that needle?

Dunno.

Far out in Nebraska, where the South Platte flows up past Julesburg, runs a highway where people have stopped to listen, for years. They say that at night sometimes you can hear a little boy crying. He's away up in those hills beyond the road; and even in modern times the folks park quietly at night, and turn off their lights, and sit listening . . . when there isn't any snow or rain, and not too much wind howling past their ears. It's then, the legend has it, that you can hear the wailing of a child. It's believed that some movers came by

there, and they were massacred, all except the little boy. He sneaked away, or else was carried up a gully by his mother or father, and left in a safe place. Or maybe he was carried off by Indians, and then abandoned instead of being killed. At any rate, he's said to be so tired and hungry and thirsty and cold and lonely, and he's wandering up there among the hills, crying for his mother. They say you can still hear him, at night. . . . Could it be? I'd like to go there sometime and listen, and see whether we might hear him still, after a long hundred years.

In calm open regions you look at the sky and listen to wires moaning and telling things, and you realize how far it is from one piece of Hamilton County to another piece.

Oh, it's far. A long way to wander.

That's what the wires strung between the posts are saying. They're humming about it.

Long way. So far . . . so far.

Chicago Calling

*N*o use in identifying the year or even the decade. Thanks be, there has always been a Fred Dempler in Hamilton County.

Always, too, there has been a Chicago calling. Sometimes its name is Manhattan or Houston or Atlanta . . . but the summons is there, to be heeded by the many, resisted by a few.

Always a patch of High Timber enriched with flower faces, to put an enchantment upon those who love the land for itself and not merely for what it yields.

There had been heavy rain during the night.

About ten a.m. Fred Dempler went out to see what had happened to his corn.

He was a slight man, round-shouldered, with long stringy muscles. You could tell that by the way his arms swung within the old blue denim jacket sleeves. Fred wore a black felt hat, crumpled and stained, but comfortable on his head. The brim was drawn into a peak above his eyes. Those eyes were solemn, gray-green; they seemed too large for his lined bony face, and strangely meditative and childlike in contrast to the middle-age which marked itself with a stubble of gray beard.

Maytime sun was warm on his shoulders. Far against the eastern horizon a haze dissolved above black rolls of wet plowing. There were a few bluebirds skimming eagerly from post to post along the lane, whistling now and again.

Suddenly Fred Dempler imagined the adjacent plowed fields as they lay in winter, when snow whitened the creases of hard frozen rolled-up earth. He saw beauty in such winter spectacle . . . didn't have to wait until spring. He hoped the weather wouldn't get too hot today. It was a lot better for this soil to dry in wind under gray skies than to be plastered stiff by the sun.

Within the field he grubbed around with exploring fingers, and turned up a few sprouted kernels, and put them carefully back into the earth once more. Germination had come rapidly . . . he thought, "Let's hope there won't be any more rain until these sprouts are well anchored."

He walked on slowly, to stand at last in the lowest corner of fencing, with long slopes stretching up on every side. Here once had been a prairie slough with blackbirds swinging and tinkling among cat-tail reeds when Fred Dempler trotted along that lane to school. It seemed impossible, yet he had to recognize the fact: that was nearly fifty years ago. Long since, layers of drainage tile had been lined beneath the soil's surface; thus the slough vanished, to reaffirm itself only after heaviest deluges.

Nearly fifty years. . . . Here he was, growing elderly, with a hearty but still-limping son freshly returned from combat in a faraway land. It was odd when he considered the gap in time between himself and Kenneth. Fred had married late. He'd never thought of himself as "the marrying type" at all, not until Etta Mapley came to teach school in that same white-painted schoolhouse where he had uttered his recitations in the long ago. And when their first child, Kenneth, was born— Well, a lot of Fred's contemporaries boasted grandchildren who were just about that little boy's age.

He recalled an occasion, nearly twenty years before, when he had driven in to town on a Saturday afternoon to do a little trading. He parked his car near the feed store, and Kenneth was standing up on the front seat, prattling the way kids do. A man whom Fred Dempler knew but slightly came over to greet him with heartiness, and to say, "Well, well, well, Mr. Dempler! I guess this must be your little grandson?" And Fred said laconically, "Nope. That's my own little boy." He noted the other man's expression, though he was still unable to say anything which might relieve their mutual—but momentary —chagrin.

In this lower corner of the huge cornfield which he still called in his mind the Old Slough, he became reassured. Less than a hundred hills were gone out on the inclines where water had rushed quickest and deepest, despite contour plowing and planting. One patch . . . oh, maybe twice the size of their farmhouse kitchen . . . where seedlings and last year's stalks and straws still simmered in a stagnant cream. There wouldn't be too much to replant. Often he'd lost ten times more new-sprouted corn at this end of the field than was apparent today. But he always planted the entire field, Old Slough and all. There were some seasons when no hills washed out. It didn't pay to miss any opportunities.

Actually Fred was not concerned merely with his arable acres. When he thought of the farm, he thought of it as a whole . . . thought of brush and pastures as well.

One area—the High Timber— meant something exceedingly important to him. Sincerely he thought it more valuable than the even-spaced flags of hybrid corn marching toward the horizon in June . . . he held notion that his High Timber was worthier treasure than oatfields when they began to turn gray and heavy, and to show a blush of yellow as July warmed them.

Shyly. "There's a kind of song in the woods, even when no birds are singing there."

And again. "I've got a thousand things to do, and here I stand. Here I stand."

He was leaning against a post which supported three strands of barbed wire. He heard the blatting of a cow, back at his farmstead. That was Julie Cow, objecting to the treatment she was undergoing. This was her fourth calf, and Fred had rather kept his eye out for milk fever. Sure enough, she got it—her first case. He rang up Doc Williams, and Doc stopped by earlier that morning. "Oh, nothing much to it." He'd blow up her udder with an Anderson pump, and tape the teats carefully, and Julie Cow would probably be all right. Actually she was the best milker in Fred Dempler's small herd. He estimated that she gave around seven thousand pounds. She had come out of an ordinary grade cow by a fine Guernsey bull belonging to the Dahlbergs next door. Fred Dempler told Gus Dahlberg that it was an Act of God, and Gus rolled up his eyes and said, "No, it was an act of my Guernsey bull." The bull had ripped down a fence to join Julie Cow's mother in her own pasture. Gus used to say that he would come around and collect all the cream offered by Julie Cow, soon as that cream was separated, to apply on the uncollectable stud fee.

Well, you had a lot of acres in corn, a lot more in oats, and you had red clover and alfalfa. Then all of a sudden there wasn't anything to do but just let nature take its course. There were times in the year like that. Oh, sure—a thousand and one things to do with and for the stock, or with machinery or with outbuildings. Also, in Fred's case, there was the High Timber to be considered.

It was his secret, kind of.

He went there in pilgrimage every spring. Some springs he went several times if he could possibly manage. It was like going to church on a weekday, and that was funny too.

Course, a modern church didn't seem as spooky as the country church, when he was a kid long ago. Nowadays you drove to town . . . on the edge of town there was the church, a flat-roofed mass of brick and limestone and glass, with a big white cross plastered on the side. To Fred's Protestant eyes, crosses meant just one thing. Catholics. But folks told him that he was living in the past . . . crosses didn't mean just Catholics any more. Might even mean

Methodists and Presbyterians and Congregationalists.

Etta said, "Don't go complaining about that cross. After all, it does show that it's a *church*. Otherwise the building looks just like that bowl-a-drome down the road a ways. Or maybe like Mr. Neshwood's under-taking place. So you'd better be glad they've *got* a cross."

When Fred Dempler was a child his folks would drive out on the prairie, three miles south and half a mile east, and tie their horse to a rail behind a willow windbreak. Then everybody tiptoed inside the church and didn't make any extra noise if they could help it. People acted stiff and self-conscious. Fred recollected that he always felt awkward and soiled and in some way sinful, even with his best clothes on. . . . They sang songs about loving God and lov-ing the church, and loving each other; but such appurtenances to worship didn't strike any answering chord in little Freddy Dempler's heart.

No more than they had in his mother's. It was the High Timber, for them. That was their church and their poem, their clandestine perfec-tion.

. . . Ma was a vigorous young woman, his father's second wife. Her eyes and her face shone whenever she moved among flowers and trees and bushes. She was more interested in green wild things than she was in raising chickens, and making butter and cottage cheese, and going to some kind of meeting with other women . . . they had the Larkin Club where all the neighbors got together and bought stuff, and saved money that way. A lot of the ladies set great store by such associations, but Fred's mother had given at best a kind of lip service.

She used to take him to the High Timber when he was just a little tyke, and how she ever got through those ravines with her skirts and all, was a wonder. One of the first things he remembered was his mother's telling him to take a nap while she dug up some plants. She had fetched along an old quilt, and it was doubled and spread out under the basswood trees, and Fred must lie on it and be very quiet.

He'd say, "But I don't want to sleep."

She'd say, "Well, you don't have to sleep, Freddy. Just lay there and watch Mother." Course, he'd always go to sleep in no time at all.

At home she had a wonderful batch of wildflowers: blue violets, yellow violets, a few white ones . . . and that taller red-and-gold-flowered plant which she used to call wild honey-suckle. (Fred found out when he was older that the true name for it was columbine.) She had bluebells growing in a dark damp corner, down a hill behind the pump at the corner of the house yard. Practically all that stuff came from the High Timber originally, but the High Timber never missed it. Gaps in the violet beds filled in quickly . . . columbine scattered seeds and renewed itself.

No, Ma was not the most efficient farm wife who ever drew breath; and Fred was certainly forced to admit that Ma hadn't been nearly as good a cook as Etta. But she was a regular Indian squaw when it came to the woods.

So his earliest memories bloomed amid moss and matted leaves of the High Timber. He always felt solemn and peaceful, and sort of wondering, when he went there.

This was a thing he wouldn't have dared to describe to Etta or to Kenneth; nor to them could he have hinted that such emotions possessed him. It was a matter which he was even timid at recognizing in himself. He tried to turn away from the knowledge of it every now and then . . . considered that he must discipline himself into being a completely practical man not given to such idiotic—even girlish—fancies.

But the feeling was too strong. It possessed him, he dared not deny it. Thus he carried it with him as a hidden grace and a hidden shame.

He journeyed to that sacred place by way of the fenced-in hilltop . . . didn't bother to open the wide metal gate. The gate gave on a cartpath which circled through pastureland alongside and beneath the High Timber . . . actually it was said to be a surviving vestige of one of the first frontier roads in the region. You could follow that path, and drive around below the mouths of ravines.

Fred skirted shallower gulleys and went into a deeper one which ran all the way down from the roadside fence. Smells of pungent life rose around him, a life growing steadily more significant beneath the sponge of last year's leaves.

He was glad he had his hat off. He had picked some mushrooms along the way . . . big knotted morels that he saw poking up through a mat of grasses here and there, and he was carrying those mushrooms in his hat. It was a good excuse for his being uncovered.

. . . Bloodroots and May-apples in leveler sections of this timberland, along a soggy precipice which fell away toward the old wheel track and the river beyond. Air and soil were cool enough to sustain a mass of hepaticas far through May. Fred

Dempler went down the hillside, sinking nearly knee deep in decaying blankets of leaves.

. . . Yes . . . white clumps, a few pink clumps, a delicate purplish clump beyond. He remembered that his mother used to call them liver flowers because of the shape of their leaves, or maybe it was his grandfather who called them that. But hepatica was a nicer name. . . . When he tripped over a rotting branch he sprawled on his knees, not bothering to rise for a moment. He turned over against the hill, with buttocks sinking into a cushion of vegetable mould.

His hand went out and brushed away some loose dead foliage beside him. The flowers nodded at him, trusting and pale on their soft wire-like stems. There was silver fuzz all along the stems, pale as the hair on a baby's skin. Fred Dempler picked one blossom. Cautiously he rolled the fragile thing between his fingers, and could see juice emerging. He lifted the scrap of flower and put it in his mouth, and quickly the taste of all the springtimes he'd ever known was on his tongue.

. . . Smell of the High Timber. Momentarily he closed his eyes in rapture. He believed definitely that God was in those woods, just as He was in the sky and clouds, and in tornadoes which whirled sometimes . . . and in thunder above. Once, on one of the rare occasions when they were talking intimately, he had attempted to relate some of these feelings to his second child, Etta Junior. Etty J. she was called. She was the only living human being to whom he would have offered such confidences.

(Etty J. had died in an automobile accident when she was in high school, several years previously. Out skylarking with a bunch of kids in a souped-up car, going too fast. They were rumored to be racing some kids in another car.)

Anyway, he'd tried to tell Etty J. some of his feelings about the High Timber. And she looked at him with wide gray eyes, and then she began to laugh. "Dad, you know what you are? You're just an old pantheist, that's what." He asked, "Pantheist? You mean I'm something like a panther?" and then they both laughed as she explained to him what she had in mind. She'd been learning about pantheists and such, in high school; but they'd never taught things like that when Fred went to school.

He whispered now, "If she meant that finding God in the woods this way— If she meant— Well, O.K. I'm a pantheist," and he smiled to himself as he lay there.

On an instant he went into rage.

He spat out the bit of flower pulp, and got up clumsily.

This was the first time he'd observed the ruination beyond, and down into the ravine . . . spreading this way and that, glimpsed through open areas between the trees. His hallowed forest was defiled . . . paper and plastic wadded or crumpled or still drifting . . . sections of Sunday newspaper with the colored funnies faded. Plates, pickle jars, beer cans, soft-drink bottles— Here grew a bumper crop of trash. Some of it might have been there since the autumn before . . . other items were much fresher.

He whispered, "They've been having a lot of picnics here," but his actual resentment burned deeper than his words.

Oh, he'd seen it before, but never on such a scale. When wild crabapple shrubbery along his fence-rows bloomed during the previous year, while Kenneth was still overseas, Fred went out to find the little trees shredded. Heavy branch after heavy branch had been torn loose, and their pink petals showed in pathetic trail all the way to the roadside, where someone had taken those glories away in a car.

Ah, there'd been bottles in the woods, and sardine cans. But never so many.

He thought, "It's the new pavement that's doing it. That fancy new fast highway." In the old days the Dempler farm was not so vulnerable, but now the county road went blind against a new highway half a mile beyond the Dahlberg house. Even those low-hung modern cars could creep with ease into pastures. There were more people on wheels every year, more ways for them to come out and despoil the countryside.

The countryside as a whole was vanishing. His lips shaped the word, he said it aloud, there was fright in the sound.

Vanishing.

By nature he was both kindly and just. So he tried, even in feebleness, to excuse Man for his forays. Fred told himself that these must be city people. It was easy for them to be heedless where mere earth and trees and bushes were concerned.

. . . Maybe they had actually looked around for a trash can to put that stuff in?

The gate was not locked, anybody could drive into the pasture. For whole days at a time, perhaps, Fred Dempler was busy, off at the other end of the farm. And the house was out of sight of the High Timber.

. . . He didn't for one moment believe that most picnickers, even city ones, would prowl deliberately into his fields and pull out crops by the roots, incited by a pure love for destruction. But the woods were something else again. So were brakes of hawthorn or crabapple or wild plum, and wild roses which grew beside them. Such areas were mere wastelands in the eyes of many farmers, and such they must appear to be in the opinion of folks who lived in towns. If you were accustomed to seeing papers and trash blowing across a parking lot every day of the year, why then you might not care how much junk you scattered around, once you were out in the country.

But this was the High Timber. He had things pressed here, treasures stowed, just as Etty J. had kept autographs and snapshots and programs of her high-school days, right up to the night of her death. She called it her Memory Book.

(Etta was sobbing when she put away that Memory Book in the trunk where Etty J.'s clothes and keepsakes were to be stored, up in the attic. Well, Fred didn't cry right then and there, not in front of Etta. It was bad enough to have her sobbing. But he went down to the barn and—)

Fred put his hatful of mushrooms aside and fell to work. It took him nearly an hour to clean out the coverts nearest him. When he had done everything he could do without tools —without a rake and a shovel and a basket or two—he had accumulated an immense pile of cans and bottles and paper. And still, beyond, he could identify many disordered fragments, baffling in their small size and scattered persistency. . . . Soon as he got time, he'd come over here with rake and shovel. This stuff was too damp to burn, anyway. And tin and glass would never burn. He'd have to bury them.

He piled a few dead limbs up across the heap, to keep it from being blown away, and walked toward his house. Peace and value of the loose woodland seemed tainted in some ugly fashion.

He remembered his mother's uncle, who lived as a bachelor in a shanty down by the river through his later years. He was a Wheeler, as was Ma. The Demplers had come from New York and Pennsylvania country stock; but the Wheelers originated in mountains of Virginia and Kentucky, and the Knobs along the Ohio River. There were critics in the community who called them a shiftless bunch, and maybe on the whole they were. They didn't care much about farming . . . always off with their dogs somewhere. In winter they liked to trap for mink and muskrats . . . in summer the children wandered along creeks, hunting for Indian arrowheads. Certainly there was more Wheeler than Dempler in Fred.

If anyone had asked him if he loved his land, he would have been embarrassed. He had read, in a few magazine stories, about farmers getting all worked up over their land . . . there was some movie wherein a man squeezed the soil between his fingers and said queer things about it. But Fred had never read any story or seen any movie which told about a farmer getting a lump in his throat merely because he smelled a worthless thicket of hazelbrush in the fall.

He wondered if he was the only man in the world who felt that way.

It would have pleased him very much if his son Kenneth were to quit talking about getting a job in Chicago, and become interested in matters about the place. Ken hadn't been very much interested in the farm before he enlisted. And now he was returned safely from out where the shooting was. It did look as if he might be lame through the rest of his life. But back in Fred's time, Kenneth would have lost that leg for sure. So Fred Dempler

guessed that Ken was just plain lucky. He couldn't stay in the Corps, and didn't want to. He had a friend who was also Out: guy from Chicago named Cady Armstrong. Cady had a swell job with some kind of electrical company, and he wanted Kenneth to come to Chicago. Cady thought he could get him a pretty good job.

Fred Dempler had been in the Corps too, long years ago. His Honorable Discharge was framed in a big closet with one window in it, which Etta had tried to fix up for him: she called it his den. But usually there was a lot of sewing and mending piled in there, and anyway Fred didn't think he really needed any den. The Discharge was on the closet wall, along with a citation which Etta framed for him. She'd wanted to put these up in the living room, but Fred said no. He said that people might think he had a Big Head, or something.

He remembered how he felt when he became a civilian once more . . . sort of like he was hung up in the air and couldn't touch the ground, and didn't know which way to turn. Sort of like he couldn't catch his breath. The High Timber had helped a lot then, but Fred feared it wouldn't exert the same influence on Kenneth which it had exerted on him.

It would be unpleasant to have their son going off to Chicago so soon after he'd come back from overseas.

·

Etta prepared fried chicken for dinner that noon; she cooked the mushrooms in thick gravy, and they tasted wonderful. It was only the second batch they'd had that year. Fred lingered at the table after Sol Havde, the hired man, had gone back to work and Etta was picking up the dishes. Kenneth still played around with a saucer of stewed apricots. He had the ruddy complexion and black eyes of the Mapleys . . . his frame was gaunt, bony, powerful. He still kept his hair clipped short.

Ken was reading a Chicago newspaper which he had bought in town the previous evening. Also there had arrived a letter with a Chicago postmark. Fred noticed the letter, hours before, when mail first lay on the table.

"What's in the news, Ken?"

"Not much." There was a lot of big type about the war on the front page, but the young man wasn't reading that.

"What about the war news?"

"The hell with it."

"Say, how about the tractor?"

Now Kenneth showed a little animation. "I got that gasket tightened, and the leak stopped temporarily. But I'm afraid that I stripped a couple of bolts. They won't hold at all, once she gets operational and banging around in the fields. I looked in all the drawers out in the work bench, and up on the shelves, but we don't have any

bolts that size. I'll have to drive to town."

Fred said, "Good enough. Maybe you can do some trading for your mother while you're in town, and there's something I want you to do for me. Stop at the printing office and get some No Trespassing signs. I understand they've got signs of all sorts, already printed, ready for sale."

Etta turned from the sink in disbelief. "You mean you're going to put up *signs* around here on the place? Why, you always said you didn't approve of folks putting up No Trespassing signs! You always said it looked kind of mean."

Dempler spoke shortly. "It is mean. But I've got to do it. You should have seen that mess of trash over in the High Timber."

"For goodness sake, what were you doing over in the High *Timber*?" Just then something boiled over on the stove, and she hurried to deal with the situation.

Her husband folded his napkin, slipped it into a celluloid clamp, and went outside. He stood on the back porch, looking off across the fields. Things were growing, you could feel them growing. He thought of how it was at night, later in the season. If you waited silently, it was as if you could feel each of the multiple seeds drilled into the soil thereabouts. You could feel and hear them, swelling and splitting each tough little skin, and sending out a fiber of pearl.

Kenneth followed his father outside, and stood filling his pipe.

Fred cleared his throat. "You know, there's a funny thing about corn. People have always been fooling with it, years before any hybrids were being offered. I read the other night in one of those Department of Agriculture books about a fellow who was planting Indian corn and experimenting with it, clear back in 1716. That was quite a while ago."

"Sure was." The young man stared in mild astonishment, as he usually did when his father got to talking that way.

Fred could reëstablish the lines of fine print on a page he had read, could remember how they looked, although he might not be able to quote them aloud.

My friend planted a Row of Indian Corn that was Coloured Red and Blue; the rest of the Field being planted with corn of the yellow, which is the most usual Colour. To the Windward side, this Red and Blue Row, so infected Three or Four whole Rows, as to communicate the same Colour unto them. . . .

Kenneth asked, "How many No Trespassing signs do you want me to get for you, Dad?"

"I guess maybe a dozen."

"Just where are you going to put them up?"

"Oh, along the fences." He started out toward the machine shed, but Kenneth followed him.

"Dad—"

Dempler turned quickly.

"I got a letter from Cady Armstrong this morning. He's positive he can get me that job, there where he works in Chicago—"

Small silence.

Fred asked, "Where is it, that Cady works?"

"Dearborn Electro-Magnetic. He makes real good money. Even new on the job—just kind of learning, as it were—he's pretty positive that I can start at about—" Kenneth named the suggested salary.

Fred told him, "That may sound like a lot of money to you, but have you got a very clear idea of how prices run in Chicago? You know—paying for lodging, and eating, and all?"

"Dad, I'm economical by nature. That's what you always said . . . you kind of bragged about it. I'm not given to extravagance. But taxes are running higher and higher, and I heard you mention that you were cramped for cash this year. Maybe after a while I'll get a good raise, and can send some money home. I guess a little extra income would be agreeable to you and Ma, wouldn't it? In hard times?"

Fred poked his son in the chest with his forefinger. "You talk about hard times. You ought to have heard your great-grandpa tell about them.

I remember he was always talking about a certain year: it was awful wet at first, and they couldn't get into the fields. They sowed wheat and oats—small acreage at that. Just before harvest it grew so wet that a black rust got on the wheat straw, and the grain didn't fill. Right at the same time, there was a red rust hit the oats, so they couldn't look forward to anything but corn. Well, the corn was slow that fall, and while the ears were still soft, millions and millions of blackbirds came swooping in and settled down over the fields. Those blackbirds cleaned out everybody in the neighborhood. Your great-grandpa and the rest of them always wondered how they ever got through the winter."

Ken shook his head sympathetically, but started toward his car. "I'll pick up those signs for you."

"Wait a minute. Let me give you some money."

"Don't bother about that."

Fred beckoned him back, and took out his wallet and withdrew a five-dollar bill. "I'm not going to have you buying signs for me. I don't care if you *are* a rich ex-Gyrene, with all that Overseas pay put away, and a check from the Government every month. This place is still mine, and it won't be yours until I die and you inherit it." He laughed. Kenneth tried to laugh too, but all he could do was to offer a guttural growl.

. . . He brought back the signs a couple of hours later. They looked ominous with their huge black letters. They said merely, NO TRESPASSING, so Fred found an old blue crayon and printed *Under Penalty of the Law* upon each card as an added threat. This was Friday, and he wanted to have the warnings in place before Sunday brought down a horde of picnickers.

He tacked the signs on small boards, and went around and nailed the boards to fences during the hour before evening chores. This was the first time that any such forbiddance had ever been posted on Dempler land. Fred thought of his father, and it seemed that his father wouldn't have approved. God knew, his mother would have liked it even less.

They loaded and hauled corn most of Saturday. Fred and Sol Havde did the loading, and Kenneth shuttled back and forth in the truck. Fred hadn't fed as many head of cattle as he'd intended, during the previous winter, and thus May found him well ahead on corn. Indeed he needed cash, so they cleaned out the west crib. That was all the corn Fred felt that he should spare to the market just at present.

Kenneth was silent and preoccupied. He said once that it gave him a funny feeling to observe those No Trespassing signs on their fences as he drove along.

His father was touched at hearing Ken say this. No, he didn't like the idea either . . . think of a man's holding some land, and then sitting back and saying smugly to the world, "No part of this loveliness belongs to you or to God. It all belongs to *me*. None of you strangers better try to share it." Nevertheless, each time he envisioned that junk over in the High Timber, he remained resolute in decision to warn malefactors away. He thought of the deal working in reverse. Thought of town folks—maybe the same ones who'd strewn paper napkins—yes, and even toilet paper—among hepatica plants— They wouldn't like it very much if Fred Dempler came into their nice church, say, and drove down the aisle on his manure-spreader. . . . This notion he kept to himself, however. Sol Havde, a stiff-necked Lutheran, would have been shocked to think that Fred considered his High Timber as religious a spot as any church.

Maybe Ken would have been appalled too? Probably.

Before Kenneth enlisted, his girl friend had been Agnes Dahlberg. They had "gone steady," except for an occasional spat, most of the time through high school, but Ken never mentioned anything about their being engaged. Agnes entered college the same month Ken enlisted. But their correspondence languished, and within a year Agnes married a young fellow whom she met at school—fellow named Byron O'Neil, called Barney by all.

Barney was just back from overseas and enjoying a furlough. He and Agnes were visiting the Dahlbergs and now some girl cousin was come for a visit also.

Etta had met the girl, Fred hadn't. They observed that Kenneth managed to spend several evenings at the Dahlberg place.

Fred asked Etta, "What did you say her name was—that niece of Gus and Gladys?"

"Marek. Viola Marek."

"That's a funny sounding name."

"Her father is of Czech extraction. You know, Bohemian."

"A Bohunk, eh?" and Fred laughed, he didn't know why. But the term Bohunk had always seemed amusing to him. One time his grandfather employed a hired man named Elmer Cepak. Elmer, who was a good-natured fellow, used to tell the boys about how he was a Bohunk and make jokes on the subject.

Etta said, "She's Gladys's sister's child, and they live in Linn County. She's a real pretty little thing. I hear she's studying to be a nurse. . . . Gladys told me that when Viola was only in her middle teens she won some kind of championship at the

State Fair. She raised a prize steer."

"What breed?" Fred wanted to know, but Etta couldn't tell him.

Saturday evening meant just one thing to the Demplers and always had. They'd go in to town and eat supper there. At the Greeks', which was the best place. That restaurant had been in the same family for over sixty years.

Saturday night, years back, the town was really crowded . . . it had thinned out a lot. Simple enough for farm families to get back and forth whenever they wanted to. So all their business activity, and socializing which they did with townsfolk— That didn't have to be crowded into a single Saturday afternoon and evening anymore.

Neither did the banks stay open Saturday night, the way they used to. There wasn't enough business to merit it.

Ken bathed and shaved and got himself dressed up, and when he came downstairs his mother told him, "You look like a million dollars."

His father said, "Well, ain't we spry? You coming in to town with us, Ken?"

"No, thanks." His black eyes turned toward them sharply. "Going to take a lady out to dinner. Drive an extra twenty miles up to Steve's Steakhouse."

Etta asked, "Same lady you've been seeing?"

He nodded. "Viola."

"Are Agnes and Barney going along?"

"No, they're going to her brother's place, in town. We may join them later. I don't know. So long," and he was gone, out to the shiny secondhand convertible he'd bought as soon as he returned to the States.

They heard the car going down the lane . . . Fred felt apprehensive, somehow. Maybe Etta did too, though neither of them spoke of it. There was this thing of having one of your children go away in a car and— When it happens to you, as it happened to them when Etty J. was killed. Well—

But Fred assured himself that he didn't feel apprehensive because of *that*. No, it was mainly a general feeling of gloom. Something going to happen, something imminent, circumstances would be changed. He shook his head, and sought to banish all dread, all worries, even vague and unidentified fears . . . he couldn't quite manage it. Though when they went to the movies, after they'd had their meal, he laughed as loud as anyone. The program was called a cartoon festival, and cartoons were Fred's favorite movie fare. Along with shorter items there was a re-showing of *Snow White and the Seven Dwarfs*. When Fred witnessed the dreadful mess which Snow White discovered in the dwarfs' house after she'd moved in with them, he couldn't help but think of the High Timber and debris which had been scattered there.

They stopped again at the Greeks' for coffee. A moment after they'd been served, Etta leaned across and whispered to Fred, "Look who's here," and Fred turned to see. The newcomers were Kenneth and his date.

"Is that her?"

"Yes, that's Viola." From then on, while they had coffee, there was nothing from Etta but a running report.

"They're sitting down now . . . they went over and looked at the machine . . . guess they decided not to play any records. . . . Yes. They're having coffee too. . . ."

Fred said, "O.K. So why not?"

". . . They're both talking a streak, leaning across the table in that booth, both of them are, and talking like all possessed. . . ."

They looked so much alike, Etta and Ken. It was one of the strongest mother-son resemblances Fred had ever observed. He meditated about it for a time. Then he told Etta, "You know, I thought Ken said they were going up to Roy Dahlberg's house."

"He just said possibly."

"Oh."

As the Demplers moved toward the cash register and the door, Ken became aware of their presence for the first time. He stood up and smiled, and beckoned them over. When she saw Mrs. Dempler coming, the young lady got up too, and welcomed her.

She was a cute little trick, no mistake. Kind of brownish-red hair, and a few freckles, and very bright dancing eyes, and manner of pride and vigor. Although she could have walked under Ken's outstretched arm.

"Viola, you haven't met my father. This is Dad."

"How do you do, Mr. Dempler? This is indeed a pleasure," the girl said somewhat primly.

Fred said, "Pleased to meet you." That was about the limit of their conversation. Because Etta nudged him. "Now, don't settle down for another cup of coffee, even though we *haven't* been invited," and everybody laughed. "Come on, it's late, we've got to be going. Tomorrow's another day."

Which was God's own truth, as any farmer knew who had to get up early and do morning chores.

". . . Well, Fred. What do you think?"

"What do you mean, what do I think?"

"You haven't said a word about her, and here we are half way home."

"Well, what was there to say?"

"Well, just— You know, if he got interested in some girl, maybe he'd change his mind."

"You mean about going to work in Chicago?"

"That's exactly what I mean. So what do you think of her?"

"What difference does it make?"

"Because she might be just the girl for him."

He said, "Oh, you womenfolks! Always thinking about marrying somebody off."

He said no more than that. Etta was in one of her talking moods, and she kept going on and on about the Dahlbergs, and Gladys said this or that, and Barney O'Neil was rumored to have a wonderful situation waiting for him as soon as he was separated from the Service.

She did remember the breed of calf which Viola had raised, and won that prize at the State Fair. Aberdeen-Angus.

The telephone began ringing when they were half way across the porch at home, after Fred had driven the car under the shed. Etta hadn't brought a key along in her purse, and she stood waiting for Fred while he put the car away. For many years they'd never thought of locking the house, winter or summer, day or night. But things were different . . . there'd been some stealing in the neighborhood . . . and one house where vandals got in and just raised hell, and actually destroyed some furniture and rugs and wallpaper. Most families now kept doors locked, when they were gone from home.

"Hurry, hurry, hurry! Don't you hear the telephone?"

Fred wanted to ask again, "What difference does it make?" But she was one of those people who always get wildly excited on hearing a telephone call. Fred hastened to unlock the door, and Etta sped across the room.

". . . What's that? Chicago calling? No, Mr. Kenneth Dempler isn't here right now. Can I take a message? . . . Operator—what number did you say? . . . Wait till I get a pencil and paper. . . ."

Chicago calling. . . .

Etta wrote it down. Ken was to ring Mr. C. R. Armstrong at such-and-such a number, after asking for Operator so-and-so in Chicago.

"I'm going up to bed." In that moment Fred felt more tired than he'd felt in weeks.

"I'll be right along. Just want to put out Ken's snack for him." She'd always done that since he was a boy. (Once upon a time there were *two* children to put out snacks for, after they'd gone off to some kind of school affair.) Fred realized that it gave Etta joy to have Ken at home, and to be able to leave the snack for him. Ken wasn't particular . . . apples, cake, strawberries . . . a plate of home-baked cookies. Etta called them hermits, and they came from an old-fashioned recipe, and were stuffed with raisins and nuts. . . . Sometimes she set out deviled eggs or a sandwich . . . always a tall glass of milk.

Fred was already half undressed by the time Etta reached the bedroom upstairs.

"I put Kenneth's snack right next to the note, so he can't possibly miss seeing it."

Fred could do no more than nod. He was too gloomy and tired. Drearily he thought, "Guess my heart's too full. As the saying goes."

Despite this he fell asleep early in the game. He slumbered while Etta was still sitting up with her tiny bedside lamp turned on, reading a Chapter from the Bible as she always did on retiring. It had not been her custom to do so in younger years, it began after Etty J.—died. She read the Bible then each evening—for solace—and thus got into the habit. Fred had permitted her to read aloud, at first; but he didn't find the surcease which his wife achieved, so he told her one night, "Probably it would be better if you just read to yourself." He would be comforted only if Etty J. were returned to life and to them, and that simply wasn't possible. The day of miracles was past. If he couldn't have the miracle he yearned for, then he didn't want to hear about any other miracles.

He dreamed. Dreamed that Kenneth was a small boy once more, and was going to run away from home. In the fantasy Fred discovered Ken's intentions when he found a list of possessions which the kid had written out, concerning personal necessities and treasures which he wanted to take along with him. Ken had noted down so many pieces of underwear, so many pairs of socks, so many neckties; blue sweater, tan sweater, work pants, tennis shoes, Scout knife; .22 rifle, ammunition— All sorts of things. Fred hurried down to the rear porch and looked out— Sure enough. There was Kenneth, hastening away across the fields, with a knapsack on his back and the .22 in his hand. . . .

Fred awoke. Despite illusion he must have been sleeping lightly. Ordinarily he didn't wake up when Kenneth came in late, but this time he did. He woke to hear Ken talking on the telephone. The young man's voice wasn't too loud . . . Fred could hear him nevertheless. Though he couldn't hear exactly what Ken was saying.

Dempler lay motionless, staring up into dimness until the rigor within him grew unbearable. Resolutely then, and moving as quietly as possible, he swung his feet out of bed and felt the chill of late spring night touching him. He fumbled around, found the jacket he had worn in to town, and with that around his pajama-clad shoulders he crept barefoot down the stairs. Light from the kitchen was reflected enough to guide him.

"Howdy, boy?" he said when he walked into the kitchen in his strange garb. This was the revival of an ancient joke. Kenneth used to put on an act when he was younger—pretending to be a hillbilly—saying, "Howdy, Pappy," and things like that. Then Fred was supposed to reply in the same fashion.

But now Ken missed on the interplay. He said, "Hello, Dad," and sat munching a ham sandwich, his hand toying with a glass which still held some milk. So deep was his concentration that when he looked at his father he seemed not to be seeing him at all.

"You got the note Mother left for you?"

"Yes, sir."

Fred pulled out a chair, and sat down and drummed his fingers lightly on the bright oilcloth.

Kenneth swallowed the last bit of sandwich, drank his milk, and pushed glass and saucer away from him. "It was Cady Armstrong."

Chicago calling.

"Anything serious?"

"He thought I'd better come Monday if I want to get that job. There's another fellow recommended by somebody else in the firm who is also in line for consideration. Cady thinks that if I come Monday, I can wrap it all up— I mean, get the job. But if I wait long, the opportunity might not be there."

"Oh, I see. You decided what you're going to do?"

Ken shook his head.

His father drew a long breath. "Well, you're a man grown. You've had a lot of rough experience—I mean, in the war. I'm not about to tell you what to do."

"It's hard to decide."

"Probably so."

Ken said, "Well, I'll have to make up my mind tomorrow. . . . It'll mean a long drive to the airport."

Fred agreed. "You'll have to start pretty early, Monday morning, in order to catch an airplane to get to Chicago during office hours."

They sat in silence for a moment, and then simultaneously stood up. Kenneth gathered the dishes on the table and went to rinse them at the sink.

He spoke over his shoulder. "Oh, Dad, something else. I won't be attending church with you folks in the morning. I'm going over to the Dahlbergs' instead. We'll go down to their Lutheran church. After that— I don't know. But don't count on me for Sunday dinner."

"I'll tell your mother."

Ken said, "Goodnight."

"Sleep tight," said Fred Dempler. This was another silly exchange which dated back to Kenneth's boyhood. Ken was supposed to speak the final line. That fell to the person who first said Goodnight.

Ken's voice seemed a trifle shaky. "Don't let the bedbugs bite." He chuckled briefly as Fred left the room and started up the stairs.

It was good to see Julie Cow on her feet instead of lying all twisted around, as when she suffered through the earlier stages of milk fever. The little heifer calf was a good one too. Very black, she looked droll beside her mottled white-and-golden mother. Fred drove them into a grassier part of the apple orchard, and Julie Cow would do well out there.

Fred mused about the Sunday dinner which Etta had prepared. Too bad that Kenneth wasn't there to help eat it. Etta certainly knew how to bake a piece of ham. She had one way, the way she'd used today, of baking ham in milk along with sliced potatoes and a little onion. She made the best cabbage salad in— Well, all of Hamilton County, her husband supposed. And homemade ice cream and devil's-food cake for dessert. That was good eating, in anybody's language.

Now Etta was sound asleep on the davenport in the parlor, and Sol Havde sat in sunshine on the back porch bench, fiddling with that old radio of his. It was an elderly set of mysterious origin which Sol kept in his room and scarcely ever played. But he was always tinkering . . . he'd bought some new parts in town

the evening before. Little gadgets wrapped in waxed paper.

Fred said to him, "Sol, you'd rather monkey around with that radio than play it."

Sol, who was years older than Fred, looked up and smiled out of his tight-lined face. "Oh, I don't know," and Sol went on humming tunelessly as he twisted his screwdriver.

Fred strolled to the north fence of the yard. Once past those trees which grew nearest the house, he could see the High Timber, or part of it. Peaks of tallest oaks still showed a blush of pink, though their leaves were large enough for a light breeze to riffle them. He remembered something his mother had told him long before, something she read in a book. It was about people of foreign nations who went softly into their churches to talk to the Lord—not just at eleven o'clock on Sunday morning, or seven-thirty of a Sunday evening, but any time they felt the need to talk to the Lord. Or, if they were Catholics, to pray to the Virgin or maybe some saint.

He looked down at his feet. No, he was still wearing Sunday shoes. Better change. He retreated to the front porch, and bent and unfastened the laces, and slipped off his shoes. In sock feet he moved quietly through the house, so that he might not disturb Etta's nap. He got a pair of work shoes, and put those on when he was back outside.

Fred strolled the lane, appreciating each moment of breath and life and springtime odor. He always called it spring, clear up to Memorial Day; then after that he called it summer.

The moment he'd passed wild gooseberry bushes which grew about the mouth of the nearest ravine, the moment he stepped among the oaks, it was as if their leaves bent and said, "We will heal you, if you need healing."

Fred wasn't much on poetry, but he remembered something from *America*.

. . . Thy woods and templed hills.

Idly, contentedly, he explored the deepest gully at his leisure. He was just clambering up a steep slope, and grasping the springy limb of a juneberry tree for support, when he stopped in his tracks.

Cars growled, down in the pasture beyond. Two cars at least, if not three. . . . He heard a sudden double slam of car doors, and men's voices talking, and the high-pitched laughter of women.

This awareness came with sickening shock, not only because of the signs he'd put up, but because he did not wish to meet anybody else in the High Timber or near it. He stood motionless, clutching the juneberry branch so tightly that it snapped beneath the tension.

I don't have to stand for this. Nobody has to stand for things like this.

He hurried up to the lane. Before he'd even reached the fence he knew what he would do. There were padlocks hanging above a work bench out in the machine-shed.

Probably it took him several minutes to get there, but it didn't seem more than ten seconds.

. . . He held a big padlock in his hand. The curved flange hung open and a key was turned in the hole. Fred twisted the key loose, put it in his pocket, and went quickly down the lane with the padlock gripped in his hand. He felt that it was a weapon . . . might have been a hand-grenade . . . something to use in a fight. He reached the pasture gate, and— Yes, there shone fresh tracks curving from roadway up through the gate, and along grass beyond. Those picnickers had closed the gate all right, for the chain was latched neatly into place. An added insult and impertinence. Not in wildest flight of fancy could Dempler believe that invaders had failed to notice that sign, prominently displayed on its post.

He craned his neck, but no cars were in sight. Possibly they had driven across pastureland and into lower woods only a few minutes before.

He fitted the padlock through opposite links of the heavy chain and snapped it shut. Steeped in hurt and resentment as he was, Fred could feel his mouth curling in a grim smile. People who went on Sunday picnics didn't usually carry wire-cutters, and few motorists were so desperate as to ruin the finish of their cars by driving headlong through fences.

This will teach you a lesson. I guess you thought it was a joke to come in here and profane these woods. Now you're going to laugh on the other side of your mouths.

When he reached the High Timber he still heard engines resounding in open places below. Maybe he'd guessed all wrong. Maybe those people were trying to leave, instead of driving in to work ruination. Maybe they'd already finished their picnic. They crept slowly, going into low gear as they inched over rotten logs which lay across the path. At this moment the thickness of the woods kept him from observing them.

He could see other things, however, when he reached the shaded slopes. Paper napkins, empty sacks, cans, glistening fabric which had covered salad bowls and wrapped cold meats . . . banana skins, orange peels . . . gaping cardboard box where ants were already busy attacking a surviving chocolate cookie. Newspapers, colored tissue handkerchiefs. Spoil of the heedless.

Fred went lower through the gully and peered between trees. At this point the ancient pasture trail crossed his vision. There were the cars, bumping away over hummocks. Yellow car and a black one, and it sounded as if another had gone on ahead.

Signs don't do any good. Maybe I'd better put out rat poison.

Returned once more to the lane, Dempler stopped between ruts and stood waiting.

Kenneth came hustling around the corner at an awkward pace which he had taught himself, lame leg or no lame leg. The knee wouldn't bend much . . . Ken traveled at what he called a hop-step-and-jump.

This couldn't be true, yet it was true.

There occurred an explosion of silver inside Fred's eyes. When his gaze cleared he watched his son approaching, and could see that he was grinning.

Yes. *Grinning.*

"Say, Dad! Somebody locked us in. Was it you, or Sol?"

Fred reached into his pocket for the key. It weighed a ton, it cooked his fingers to the bone.

"Here you are."

"This is quite a joke on me! Agnes and Barney, and the Nettleton boys and their dates, and Viola— See, after church we thought we'd take a picnic lunch out in the timber somewhere. Of course the Dahlbergs haven't got any timber on their land. So the girls fixed a few refreshments in a hurry, and we fellows drove by the store at Casey's filling station and got some drinks and other stuff. Viola wanted to pick wildflowers, she said, and I told her there were plenty over here. Guess you must have heard the cars? Anyone can hear the Nettleton boys in that old crate of theirs, two miles away!"

Fred said, "I heard the cars." He dropped his hands into his pockets, then took them out again, and managed to wave a finger in Ken's direction. "Better get along. They're all likely in a hurry—"

Ken dashed away, with automobile horns pressing him into speed again.

. . . Fred stopped at the farmstead and fetched a spade and a garden rake, and a can of kerosene. Probably he should have changed his clothes. Have to be careful and not get these Sunday clothes dirty. . . .

Scrap by scrap he assembled the debris. It made quite a pile. *You wouldn't think that eight young folks could leave such a mess.* And look here— Somebody had trampled a clump of hepaticas . . . must have

been an accident. No one who loved wildflowers would have done that deliberately.

Today's stuff was dry, but the refuse he'd scraped together on Friday was still damp. Good thing he'd thought to bring kerosene. Bottles and tin cans wouldn't burn—that was why he'd brought the spade.

Smoke drifted up from two fires, puffing and slanting among afternoon sunbeams. It didn't carry the smell of an autumn bonfire . . . leftovers of potato salad and beans simmered as paper plates dissolved . . . they made a bubbling whisper before they charred. Dempler tended the fires carefully to prevent their spreading into dry leaves beyond. He'd sit here, and watch; then after everything was burned up, he'd rake fresh earth and leaves to cover the scorched or dug-up areas.

He heard a trampling in woods behind him, and here was Kenneth limping along the hillcrest, twirling that padlock on his forefinger. "Here." When he reached Fred Dempler's side. "Give me the rake, Dad."

"I'm about through, Ken. You know—" Fred tried to keep his voice steady. "You people made quite a mess down here."

"Don't I know it! Papers blowing, and everything. But I figured it'd be easy for me to come back and take care of matters later on. You know—"

He lowered his voice. "If we were having a party over at the house, we wouldn't make everybody stay and straighten the parlor before they went home, would we? I don't recall your ever having done so."

His father looked at him in some amazement. "No, I guess you're right. We wouldn't ask them to stay and clean up."

He squatted on his haunches, pushing last embers together with the rake. Kenneth sat on a log across from him.

"Dad, there's something else. I've been thinking. Those signs really look terrible."

"Signs?"

"I mean the No Trespassing signs."

"Seems like they're necessary."

"I don't agree. Dad, if people are going to break off blossoms—crabapple and plum and wild cherry and so on—they'll do it anyway. Signs or no signs. Folks like that always will. But all we need to do is put this padlock on the pasture gate, and keep it locked. If anybody wants to have a picnic here in the brush, they can come up to the house and get the key. I could tack a card on the post, to that effect. Then you or I, or maybe Sol Havde, could kind of warn them about picking everything up after they were through with their fun. You know: leave the place the way they found it."

Fred told him, "They'd surely have to travel a long way to get *your* opinion on the subject. All the way to Chicago."

There sounded a light scratching in undergrowth behind them, as if a tiny rooster were tearing old leaves apart. But when the creature came into view it proved to be a bird marked with chestnut and black and white.

"Ground robin," said Fred.

Ken shook his head. "No, that's a towhee. Or cheewink—that's another name for them, count of the little whistle they make. Sounds like he says 'Cheewink?' "

"Maybe so. Your grandmother used to call them ground robins."

Kenneth tried to make a *cheewink* sound, and the bird flew away in fright.

"Nobody will have to go to Chicago to talk to me, Dad. Because I won't be in Chicago. I'm going to be right here."

Last coals of smoldering wreckage, glowing flakes of cardboard and corrugated paper—they wavered before Fred's gaze. Ah, there weren't enough heat waves in these small fires to make a thing like that happen.

He heard himself. . . . "You—altogether certain about that?"

Ken had lighted his pipe. He puffed a while in silence. Then—

"Last night when I went to bed, I couldn't sleep. You know—considering, weighing the pros and cons. Then

I got to thinking about the place. I'm well aware, Dad, that you used to laugh—I guess you might call it *ruefully*—and say that you didn't think I was cut out for a farmer. I remember, when I was a little boy, you said that the only thing I liked to do was to gather eggs."

Fred was smiling. "You sure did like to gather eggs every evening! Like it was a treasure hunt." He realized that he was blinking rapidly.

". . . Seemed like the High Timber got in the way, every time I tried to think about that job in Chicago. Then I'd think of leaving you short-handed. Just you and Sol to do so much that's got to be done on the place. Corn ploughing, all the way up into July; and after that the oats. And of course there'll be the first crops of hay and alfalfa to be cut. . . . You know, I thought of something else. Wouldn't this be a nice place to build a house? Right up above, on the edge of the High Timber? Where you can look off across the valley? Quite a view."

Fred agreed. "It would be a real nice place to build a house. How would you finance it?"

"Oh, you know I've got a little money saved. The rest would be on a GI loan. It could be managed."

"You thinking in terms of that little girl Viola?"

Ken nodded. "I guess she and I are both thinking in the same terms.

There's worse places to spend one's life than right here. Viola feels the same way."

Fred put down the rake because his hands were unsteady, and there was nothing he could do but sit upon them for a while. Even his spareness pushed the fingers deep into leafy soil . . . he could feel the tonic of native earth flowing upward into his body. As if he had actually taken root there.

A woodpecker began to hammer against a dead limb above their heads, and they both looked to see it.

"A flicker," said Ken.

Fred told him, "Yellow-hammer."

Ken squinted and watched the golden-brown bird working jerkily along the limb. "Some people call them high-holers, too."

His father insisted stoutly, "Ma called them yellow-hammers. There's always been a lot of them in the High Timber."

The Taste of Cider

*Y*ou are growing taller, and you know exactly what's in a certain building set far back from the corner at Elm Street and Willson Avenue. But there was a time when you didn't know. In those very first years, Downtown was a long way to walk, so your mother pushed you in a stroller. When you came to that place with concrete curbings around the edge, you'd wave your arms and cry out in glee— *Uhhh,* you said at first, but Mamma realized what you were demanding, even before you'd learned to speak the word *Up.* Thereupon she'd let you climb from the cart, and she'd lift you atop that curbing (so very high it seemed when you were small) and your face would be one vast grin. She'd hold your hand and you'd prance delightedly, marching the length of the curbing, or stepping gallantly along the lawn inside.

. . . There came a day when you were bold enough to climb up on the blunt knob which grew at the corner and— Yes. Jump off. First with Mamma helping you; but before long you could jump off *all by yourself.* And not fall down, either.

This winter, this day, you are of a generation far removed from that of tiny folks in strollers. You're halfway through Second Grade, and you can read like anything. Teacher told Mamma that you're one of the best readers in her class.

When you were baby-sized you used to wonder what was inside the building beyond the great-big-high curb (it doesn't seem so high anymore). But you didn't have sense enough to ask, not for quite a while. Then, when finally you did ask, you were told, "That's the library," and you repeated the word questioningly. "Ly-bury?"

*I*t is like tasting your first apple, if you could remember when you did so.

. . . Fat firm pleasant apple, but soft and tangy inside, with tiny silver crystals of moisture showing when you bite off a piece. And streaks on the shining skin—redness and pinkness and yellow, and a shade of green still left, variegated and intermingled. And then, when you bite, there is that flavor. . . .

As if you were munching perfume, and hearing the starchy rustle of autumn leaves when folks rake them up to burn and to build a matchless odor in their very vanishment.

Ah, there is trifling fear as well . . . notion of spooky trees, and midnight shadows over tombstones, and menace waiting there. But some sort of menace pervades all existence, so the sooner we find that out, the better.

*O*ur Mr. Smith is reading to us students, and we follow the reading along with him.

. . . *Inveterate propensity of their husbands to linger about the village tavern on market days.*

(It is somewhat difficult to be confronted with "inveterate propensity.")

. . . *The cognomen of Crane was not inapplicable to his person.* That was in the first part, which we had when we began to read last Monday. But it's not really fair to dwell on these five-leggèd words. Truly there was so much which we could understand and laugh at, right away . . . when it talked about his hands dangling a mile out of his sleeves; and his feet that might have served for shovels; and his large green glassy eyes; and the long snipe nose perched upon his spindle neck, to tell which way the wind blew.

Then, when it described the schoolhouse, we could scarcely believe that anyone had ever gone to school in a place like that . . . *windows partly patched with the leaves of old copy books.* . . .

Wouldn't it be wonderful to sit spinning by the fire, with a row of apples roasting and sputtering along the hearth?

. . . And withal a provokingly short petticoat, to display the prettiest foot and ankle in the country round.

I wonder what Ichabod Crane and Washington Irving and all those folks would have thought, if they could have seen girls in miniskirts? I guess maybe they wouldn't have believed it.

We had *Rip Van Winkle* before this. I think the boys liked that better than the girls.

Still, we are all enjoying *The Legend of Sleepy Hollow.* While we were having lunch yesteday, some of us talked about the parts that we liked best. Some kids liked to hear about Ichabod and his school, but everybody enjoyed the descriptions of food.

When food is mentioned, it always sounds nicer than anything we eat in a cafeteria . . . pigs running around with puddings in their bellies, and pigeons put to bed under a coverlet of crust, and geese swimming in their own gravy. . . .

And buckwheat cakes and things.

We had some cider to drink at a party last Halloween. I think this story reminds me of cider. It sort of tingles.

At first I thought Ichabod Crane was a rat fink, the way he whipped those scholars in his school, but now I'm not so sure. I begin to feel kind of sorry for him.

*F*irst wondering adventure, first adventurous wonderment . . . beginning of awareness that there was another time, a time seemingly unrelated to your own.

Places which did not appear as they appear today (yet you can see them, if you peer through those clear windows: the pages of a book).

Earliest realization that there is, in truth, an enormous complicated pattern called the Past . . . and books are a door, too; and we go through, and there we stand, for better or for worse.

And the vague notion that books mean different things to different people. That in itself is mysterious.

Oh, suddenly—

Can you recognize this enchantment?

Yes, yes!

Can you explain it?

No, not yet. Perhaps never. But—

Let me read *more*.

You hold in your hand a key, a bullet, a spy-glass, a kiss. What is this thing which can be all things to you?

It is a book.

*Big
Lively
Round
Ball*

*I*n most portions of Hamilton County, throughout the winter months, scholastic basketball occupies the attention and energy and emotion of young people to an extent which would have seemed unbelievable to those who lived in the days before basketball was invented by one nice Mr. James Naismith for his YMCA classes. That happened in Springfield, Massachusetts, in 1891.

In the United States alone, more than one hundred and twenty million people were spectators at the games last year. Thus it seems odd to realize that, statistically, there are many millions of Americans still living who are older than basketball itself.

(Maybe so. But I remember being guided over scorched terrain under the Yucatan sun, until we stood on a paved court next to the ruins at Chichen-Itza or Uxmal or one of those places. I asked our guide about a stone ring cemented against the ancient wall, and he said that the Maya used it in a game they played. The idea was to toss a ball through that stone ring; and the idea of the opposing team was to prevent you from doing so. Kind of like basketball, wasn't it? . . . Except that the captain of the losing team paid a gentle little forfeit: he had his heart cut out of his body. Those Maya really played for keeps, whether they called it basketball or no.)

In the days when this author went to school in his home town in Hamilton County, we had a player named Merritt Greeley. He was a popular boy . . . for some reason his nickname was Dog. Dog Greeley was the star shooter of our school team. That was before rules were amended to compel any player who was fouled—and thus gained a free throw—to try for that extra point *himself*. Not so in 1922. Whenever a team was awarded a free throw, some man on the team who specialized in this art could undertake the shot from the established free throw line: fifteen feet from the basket.

Dog was an unimpressive figure—flat-chested, lounging in his gait. Not the beau ideal of a basketball player or any other sort of athlete. . . . Well, one day he had a little falling-out or a little run-in, whatever you want to call it, with the basketball coach. This seems mysterious now; but I can't call up Merritt Greeley on the telephone and ask him what that dispute was all about. He has gone to a Realm where Long Distance does not function.

He was in fact a mild-mannered youth, easy-going as to disposition. Maybe the coach, himself very young at the time, decided that he must establish an awesome reputation as a martinet. Whatever the reason, he banished Dog Greeley. Our best shooter, and he was thrown off the squad.

What it amounted to was wiping out our team's chances for the rest of the year. Oh, sure—there were a lot of good players still left on the squad. But since every team always had a specialist for free throws, we were handicapped. Our team went down to defeat, game after game.

People came around and pleaded with the coach to reinstate Greeley, but he said that they were just wasting their time.

Greeley went to all the games just the same. He sat in the audience on the sidelines and punished himself for whatever sins he'd committed, in watching the rival teams' triumph.

Until you've seen a high-school basketball game with the crowd going wild. . . . Well, I guess you hain't seen nothing yet, far as young people are concerned.

. . . So it was the end of the first half, with the home team behind, visitors leading. Say it was Visitors 34, Home Team 31. Had we been able to capitalize on free throws subsequent to the fouls, we would have been well ahead. But the boys who tossed the balls weren't displaying any accuracy. Each time a ball toppled clumsily off the backboard a groan would go up from the home towners who clogged balconies and benches; and a shriek of glee would rise from the smaller mass of visiting fans in their special section.

. . . So the whistle had blown, and players went darting off to the locker rooms. And, for some reason or other, some official allowed the ball to get away from him. I guess he tossed it to another official, and the other official missed the catch.

Anyway the big lively round ball went rolling and bouncing all the way down the playing court to where Dog Greeley sat on a front row bench in his shabby sweater. The ball came and kissed against his ankle, as much as to say, "Hi, Greeley. Where you been lately?"

Dog sort of sighed. He leaned over and took the ball between his hands. He stood up and—

The basket at the far end of the court was over a hundred feet away as the crow might fly (if any crows had been flying in that gym). With the same easy motion, as he lifted the ball in his hands and as he rose, Dog tossed it the length of the playing court. The ball sailed high and far. It dropped through that basket so easily that it scarcely disturbed the mesh hanging from the ring.

You ought to have heard the wail which went up from local fans. Our coach, belatedly heading for the locker room, had turned around, and he saw the whole thing. He stood for a moment, hands on hips, glaring at Merritt Greeley. Then he turned toward the door. Greeley had slouched back on his bench once more, and gave a big yawn.

The fury of the crowd followed the coach all the way to the door. Booooo . . . booooo . . . *booooo!*

Nearly fifty years later, another coach says, I'm going to put you in there for Oscarsen. You remember to pop it to Fushard, underneath. I'll bet I've told Oscarsen to do that a hundred times, so that's why he's coming out of the game. Now listen, Buster. We're playing a three-two zone press, and dropping into a one-two-two. Get in there and do a job, see?

*A*home town crowd in Wright County watches the visiting team from Hamilton County, right next door. Too bad . . . they don't know it now, but the Hamilton County team is going to win.

The young, the oh so tender young, the bellowing, the squealing, the strong, the bright ones, the dullards, the way-out types, the square types; the ones just ready to graduate and thus achieve that momentary elation of maturity; little brothers and sisters fetched along; everybody's got to go to the game, everybody would die if they couldn't go to the game; pity the absent people at home with flu, or maybe they slipped on the ice and got a broken arm or a broken ankle, and they couldn't go to the game; look at them, try to hear them if you can, no you can't truly hear them, your ears won't accept the tempest, the whistles, the shrieks, the howls, the hullabaloo; it isn't the cheerleaders who are doing it . . . see them sitting up there on that barricade, watching, resting between bouts of more studied cheering, doing their personal yelling about the game.

Coach says, Twelve always does the same thing. Get this now: he does a double pump left, then shoots or drives right. Don't follow his fake, and you'll have him bottled up. Make him prove he can drive left.

Oh yes, get Wickstrom out of chaser, and back underneath the basket. It's only the second quarter, and he already has three fouls.

*T*hese players aren't from Drake or Tulsa, they're not from Purdue or UCLA, they're not any players from North Carolina. But— Who knows? Maybe one of these times some of them will be starring for Drake University. You never know.

They might not look like All-Americans, but they all look like Americans.

Who can guess what blows will strike those youthful faces in the crowd, or estimate the joys that will charm them? What will life do to a bespectacled blonde cheer-leader who somehow got mixed up with the audience; and what will she do to the lives around her? What will the years bring to a plump-faced girl with a wide-open mouth, to a meditative little boy in sneakers, to another blonde who presses her hands together in an agony of prayer; and, in turn, how will *they* affect the decades ahead?

(Let us laugh in unison, and discontinue such idle speculation. Neither you nor I know what life will offer us—next week, or next month, or to-morrow, or in the next ten minutes. Nor, in turn, do we know just whom we will hurt, or whom we will sustain.)

Switch to a four zone, with Brayce playing man-to-man on Twelve. You and Fushard get underneath, and McCool and Wickstrom outside. . . . If Twenty-two or Thirty-two prove they can hit, play a four man-to-man, with Wickstrom dropping off Forty and playing zone.

I can't win this game from the bench. It's up to you guys out there on the court. Just play like you have all year, and you can take this game.

*I*n my special portion of Hamilton County there was a village named Kamrar with a few hundred people living in it. The town is still there—what's left of it. You know how things go these days: so many villages fading away. . . . No trick now for a customer to drive eight or eighteen miles to the county seat in winter to do some shopping; or go to the bank, or consult an attorney, or negotiate about shipping cattle, or do whatever it is he has to do. He's eight or eighteen miles away, and maybe it takes him eight or eighteen minutes to get to town.

There was a time when eighteen miles would have taken the whole day. The whole day and then some, in bad weather.

Kamrar boasted an elevator and an antique railroad station sitting there on that branch line. Mr. Hoyt, the agent, lived upstairs over the station and— Let's see. Oh yes, the Havinga family had a store . . . and didn't the Jaycoxes have a store, too? There used to be a tiny bank on the corner; and a fellow I knew went to work in that bank, and one day he shot himself through the head, we never knew why. Some folks said that he had stolen money from the bank, but others said, "No. It was ill health."

There were those few houses scattered around, and the schoolhouses; and then, in every direction, roads stretched out into the country. That was where the majority of the kids lived who went to school.

So what about Kamrar?

This about Kamrar. In 1948, the girls' basketball team of Kamrar went down to the tournament in the State capital, and they won the State championship. That's right, they *won* it. Country girls from an obscure hamlet, climbing to the top over every other school in the State.

In that portion of Dallas County which lies in the State of Texas, there was a girls' team from a big place called Mesquite—population of twenty thousand or so—and they won the Texas State championship, and were looked upon as maybe the best team in the United States. So what happened? They played Kamrar, and the Kamrar girls beat them by a score of 36 to 33. When everybody from Kamrar drove back to Hamilton County after the game— They say that no one in the area got a wink of sleep that night. They were too busy celebrating.

How's about a photograph of those 1948 Kamrar girls? (I do possess such a picture. It was the work of a Des Moines *Register* photographer in that same season.) There were twelve girls on the squad, and the names of some mean a lot to me because I went to school with their parents, and knew their grandparents, at least many of them.

. . . Know something? There's not an ugly babe on the team. Not one. They look like a bunch of bathing beauties dressed up in basketball uniforms. They look like Rockettes. They look eager and healthy and full of humor, and full of desire for existence, and desire for attainment, and desire to be good wives and mothers, and to be happy, and to make people about them happy.

They look perfectly beautiful.

Don't they?

KAMRAR—STATE CHAMPIONS—1948

You Should of Heard What Barbara Said

*I*f you're a boy, Youth is a hot iron bar.

Youth wakes you up at night. Then you lie wondering, considering Her of whom you've just dreamed.

She may be the girl who sometimes sits across from you on the school bus; or possibly the girl who works opposite you in Chem Lab; she may be Miss Brolley who teaches you Humanities; she may be—Heaven help us!—the elder married sister of your friend Harris who lives just around the corner; she may be that girl whom you met at the party last New Year's and you hadn't thought of her since. She may be any female of whom you've ever been aware; or someone you've seen briefly on the TV screen; or someone conceived only in that same erotic dream, a person fleshed alone by your slumbering imagination.

Whoever she may be, she too is a portion of that same cryptic haunting luring thwarting Youth which baits you every waking hour . . . and now through the sleeping hours also.

*Y*ou should of heard what Barbara said.

What did she say?

Oh, I guess I'd better not tell you. God, is it a riot!

Well, if it's so funny as all that, you'd better tell me.

Oh, I guess you wouldn't think it was funny.

I'll promise to laugh if you want me to. You shouldn't of brought it up if you're not going to tell me.

Tell you what?

Look, man, don't give me that or I'm going to kill you.

I don't know what you're talking about, actually.

Man, you act so innocent it makes me sick! You best cool the jokes and tell me what she said.

What who said?

Uh. I forgot.

*I*f you're a girl, Youth is a mystery too complex to be solved, and so you pretend that you own the full solution, and preen yourself accordingly . . . before your parents, before all boys, before the entire world . . . quickly you flee into hysterical secrecy, weeping because in fact you understand nothing, truly nothing. Nobody understands you, nobody appreciates you, you don't know what to do about your hair—it's too coarse, it's too curly, it's too fine, it's too straight— Oh, if you were only tall like Sharon! Oh, if you were only petite like Michelle! Oh, if you were only a svelte brunette like Carlotta! Oh, if you were only a dainty blonde like Tricia Nixon! If Roger Drighton would only look twice in your direction, in the cafeteria— If Levin the swimming coach weren't married to that gross little wife of his— If Paul Newman would only come to town for a personal appearance—If Prince Charles weren't away over there being royalty and everything, and went to school here instead—

If, if, if, if only—

And you haven't anything *fit to wear.*

. . . Then, fully conscious and ready for the fray, you step out into a clamoring society, and you are Woman once more, wrapped in your shimmering costume of self-assurance and enticement, and with a mask of bored sophistication stenciled on your face.

God go with you. . . .

You are time-bomb and disaster, infant and sibyl, illness and remedy.

You have all the answers. (You have none.)

Vaya con Dios!

*H*ey, guess what just happened!

I give up. What?

Barbara and Scoot just broke up.

They did? I thought they'd never break up, they looked so good together. Who broke up with who?

Barbara broke up with Scoot. Now she likes Richard.

Richard makes me sick . . . he thinks he's a real cool head.

I knew it was coming. She hasn't liked him for the last two weeks.
You claim you did know? How come you ever kept a secret like that?
Man, if I knew a thing like that, I would of had to tell somebody.
Yeh, you would. That's why I didn't tell you.

Your energy could alter the landscape on which Humanity gazes, were you able to direct it so. (You cannot.)

Your vitality is a visible substance, it possesses dangerous tactility . . . an elder person may barely touch it and be burned.

Your power is fierce, unruly, it spins as a tornado spins, it can exalt, it can ruin.

It must be trained, tamed, seasoned, while you squall that you have been impinged upon.

*T*hen I have a thirty-page term paper to do, two recitations, a character study, World Cultures homework . . . what a drag!

Man, am I glad I don't have MacBlaren! I don't even get through with the work I already have.

Well, you probably think I'm a tread, but I don't mind writing that term paper. It's really interesting. MacBlaren is sort of weird, but she's a good teacher.

Yeh? I think you're a tread.

A tread. . . .

Fifty years ago we said "a grind."

Fifty years ago we were as alive with your own Youth—as entranced, as baffled, as berserk, as prodigal.

Fifty years from now. . . ?

It'll be a tough row to hoe, Youth of the early Twenty-first Century. No matter how many tracks have been made upon the Moon . . . or Mars.

Auntie Tate Lives Down The Avenue

Trees are so very tall.
I have heard about mountains.
The trees must be mountains.
They talk to me when I go past, with Kitty in
    my arms.
We are going to Auntie Tate's.
Auntie Tate lives down the avenue.

. . . Kitty is named Midnight, but usually we just
say Kitty.
. . . Mamma had some old white shoes. She was
going to throw them out; but I said, "Please give
them to me." So Mamma gave them to me.

I play that the trees are people. I have named
many of them, but no one else knows this.
I whisper their names when I walk by them, and
under their shade.

Auntie Tate will give me an apple, or maybe some
cherries or plums. She will make me use a paper
napkin, and wash my face and hands after I eat.
She will pour condensed milk into a saucer for
Kitty. Sometimes Kitty drinks it, sometimes not.
. . . Why?
. . . My Lady shoes keep coming off.
. . . Why?
. . . The trees keep saying things, gently.
. . . Why?

I have heard about God.
Maybe the trees are God.

Feathered Friends

*D*o not forget the birds these wintry days, when snow lies deep and the daylight time is short," wrote Miss Myrtle Dunaway. "We may coax many birds into our dooryards if we will. The simplest way of alluring the birds is to affix a piece of beef suet to the trunk of a tree, high enough for dogs and cats not to jump up and eat the birds. Nail it—or fasten in a mesh of chicken-wire—where you can watch from the windows of your home and keep watching during the day, for surely birds will come and peck at the suet. Woodpeckers—downy, hairy, and redheads —also brown creepers, nuthatches, chickadees, and juncos. If you are lucky you may get a tufted titmouse, and last week a redbird came to mine. Soon they will tell all the other birds, and you will have a regular procession. Also, you will see that no two varieties of birds will peck at the suet at the same time."

She carried her manuscript to the office of the weekly newspaper. This item (she called these letters *Items,* and they were not signed with her name but always marked *Contributed,* although everyone knew who wrote them) appeared the following Thursday.

Before five-thirty on Thursday, in the first cold darkness which throttled Myrtle Dunaway's house on West

Adirondack Street, and when Miss Dunaway was out in the kitchen getting supper for herself and her cat— The telephone rang.

She knew who was calling, even before she reached the phone . . . because she'd had an Item in the paper. Few people ever telephoned her except members of the Ladies' Aid.

"This is A. J. Pallentine speaking."

"Yes?"

"Did you write that thing in the *Ledger*?"

"Well, I had a kind of an Item—"

"You made a very, very serious error that's got to be corrected!"

"I don't know what you're talking about," lied Miss Dunaway.

"—That part where you say two birds of different species won't come to suet at the same time—"

"It's absolutely true."

He roared, "You'll have to make a retraction, Myrtle Dunaway! Last week I had three chickadees eating at my bird feeder, and some tufted titmouses came right down beside them and started to eat. I can prove it, too! I called my wife and she saw them. And one time I had a cardinal and two bluejays feeding together, just as friendly as could be! And I had—"

"There must be some mistake," said Myrtle Dunaway primly.

She repeated these words until Mr.

Pallentine's voice became merely a succession of grunts at the other end of the wire.

"I am of the opinion, Mr. Pallentine, that what you saw were just some more chickadees coming to eat, and not tit*mice*—" she accented that word shrilly—"at all. I doubt very much that you ever saw a redbird in company with bluejays."

"Myrtle Dunaway," resounded Pallentine's hoarse attack, "you better be careful about how you go around giving the lie to folks! You may have forgotten that I'm local chairman of the SPCA; and people have got their opinion of anybody who goes around writing articles about birds, and then keeps a great big hungry tomcat for years on end—"

Hannibal came and rubbed against Miss Dunaway. She beamed down at him, and stood for a time defending Hannibal's reputation. She quarreled with Pallentine for five more minutes. Then they both hung up, although this time Mr. Pallentine really hung up first.

Hannibal cantered ahead to the kitchen, his bell tinkling with a fairy note. It was hung around his neck, on a soiled strand of red ribbon which did not seem to be tied tightly; yet Hannibal never lost his bell. He was a short-legged broad-shouldered cat with a square brutal face and a fatuous expression. Miss Dunaway fed him chopped liver in the morning and salmon at night, and she contended that no cat thus fed (especially if he were properly belled) would try to catch birds, or at least ever succeed in catching them. She hated most other cats with unquenchable ferocity, and kept a BB gun in the kitchen—an old one, with which she shot at stranger felines invading her garden. She had never been known to hit any.

Hannibal was a born fighter . . . always coming in with face blood-smeared and dirty, and ears scratched raw. None of the neighbors had much use for Hannibal . . . especially since that time when Mrs. Walterick published abroad her complaint of the half-eaten robin she had glimpsed under a honeysuckle bush at the corner of Miss Dunaway's lawn . . . and of the fluffy yellow feather which someone else saw glued to Hannibal's whiskers, a week or two later. Still, no one had ever caught him in the act, and probably never would catch him, since Hannibal was extraordinarily crafty.

His mere presence discouraged birds. Myrtle never stood much chance of competing with A. J. Pallentine in numbers and species of visiting boarders recorded.

Excepting for Boy Scouts and their leader, Myrtle Dunaway and A. J. Pallentine were the only Hamilton County citizens who fared forth for the avowed purpose of observing birds. Pallentine often spoke of them as "our feathered friends," but to Miss Dunaway's credit she never called them anything but birds.

Mr. Pallentine had conducted a stationery and confectionery store until his brother died in Schenectady and left him a sizable estate. He lived in a house two blocks east of Miss Dunaway's home, with a wife sadly crippled by arthritis. He had an expensive pair of German binoculars, complete with heavy russet leather case, which he wore on a strap around his neck. In spring months especially his familiar fleshy figure—his pouchy face with its drooping eyes and well-kept mustache—was often seen among pines and cedars of the cemetery, or in more distant glades alongside the lake.

Miss Dunaway, on the other hand, preferred to explore the meadows, higher hills, and brushy pastures adjoining Kindeling's horse farm. Her own binoculars were old and scratched; truly they were nothing but moderate-priced opera glasses in the first place, and part of their mother-of-pearl coating had been broken off. Myrtle carried them in the pocket of her red plaid lumberjack coat.

Her hair was frizzy, and she dyed it

orange. She had small brown eyes, sallow skin, freckles, and uneven greenish teeth. She had never possessed a male friend since she left high school and became deputy under her father, the county treasurer. But more than one man declared that Myrtle Dunaway used to have real pretty legs. . . .

Now her legs were skinny, because she had lost so much weight; but Hannibal liked to purr against them.

On one unfortunate occasion the Scoutmaster carelessly requested both Miss Dunaway and Mr. Pallentine to serve as judges in a birdhouse-building contest. Of course these two quarreled, and had entirely different ideas about which birdhouses were best, though Myrtle won the third judge to her support . . . Mr. Pallentine called up Mrs. Dolly Duchaine and told her that her son Paul should have had first prize instead of fifth.

The Scoutmaster dreamed no longer of an idyllic day when he would come upon Myrtle Dunaway and A. J. Pallentine companionably examining fox sparrows in a thicket. To his mind it was absurd—the whole sputtering voluble feud. Also it was absurd to the minds of many others who could not understand the warped neurotic rivalry which sustained these two.

More than one sentimentally inclined person, whose rigid morality did not preclude intimate imaginings, had dreamed a tender pastoral in which Miss Dunaway and Mr. Pallentine became autumnal lovers—as might well happen, even with a man of his age, when arthritis chilled and twisted his home.

But almost no one realized that in their petty conflict there were included elements of that respect which is born of long-lived antagonism.

Myrtle Dunaway, had she been told that Pallentine dropped dead the night before, would not have looked out at her feeding-tray with the free gaze of yesterday.

A. J. Pallentine was to experience a similar aimless sense of loss—honed clean and sharp by their mutual masochism—in the hour when first he learned how Myrtle Dunaway had come to a lonely trampled obliteration in Louis Duchaine's bull pasture.

Business With Bankers

Shortly after three o'clock in the afternoon, three bank officers—Sterling French, L. T. Hyatt, and Ralph Togland—came into the Olympia Lunchroom.

An aisle led from the front door to a wider part of the restaurant near the kitchen. As they walked to the rear, the men seemed to fill that entire space, between a long watery mirror on the wall and a row of stools alongside the counter.

There was only one customer in the lunchroom at that hour—a boy in blue coveralls, enjoying Danish pastry and coffee. The old cook and his two pretty daughters, who washed dishes and prepared roasts and vegetables in the kitchen, were gone until four-thirty. Bill Zanias himself could take care of any short-order trade in the meantime. Should a steak be desired, he would fry it on the hamburger and sausage fryer just inside the front window.

He left off rolling tenderloins as soon as the three bankers entered. Although he knew them, and might guess why they had come, he wiped his hands on a towel and filled three glasses with water before he approached the porcelain-topped table where the men seated themselves.

Bill Zanias was not tall. He had the neck and shoulders of a wrestler, but even in his thirties a slight paunch was showing under the stained apron he wore. His curly hair was brown with sandy lights in it; and his small

dark eyes seemed perpetually sad and compassionate.

The handsome blondish Sterling French looked up at Zanias as he came round the end of the counter. "Bill, can you spare a few minutes?"

"Sure, Mr. French." Bill stood with the three glasses balanced skillfully on his broad stubby hand.

Ralph Togland smiled. Mr. Togland's face was not made for smiling, but he achieved horrors in this pursuit many times each day.

"Bill's always got plenty of time," said L. T. Hyatt comfortably. His plump oval mouth was made for disbursing genial pleasantries, as surely as Togland's was not.

Bill said, "I always got plenty time." A giggle stole up within him, but died before it reached his throat. He still held the cool glasses. Pearls of moisture gathered on them. . . .

Sterling French ran his forefinger halfway around the inside of his limp collar. "Want to sit down a minute, Bill?"

Zanias glanced toward the front door and said something about customers.

"The hell with customers," said Ralph Togland. "We want to talk important business with you, Bill." Again his face became terrible. He showed all of his upper front teeth . . . white clean teeth, large and square.

Bill Zanias clinked the three glasses softly. Water spilled from one, and he moved his foot quickly to avoid having his shoe splashed. Once when he was fifteen, and working in his uncle's place in Philadelphia, his foot had been badly burned when boiling grease splashed upon it. "You want to talk about the banks?" he asked.

French and L. T. nodded in self-conscious courtesy.

Bill put the glasses down on the table.

Togland began to play with the cover of a sugar bowl. But he was watching Bill all the same, and Bill knew it.

"This has got to be on the Q.T.," said Hyatt. "Q.T. from L.T." He laughed. Sterling French tried to join him, producing only a cackle.

Ralph Togland smiled again. "I don't think Bill gets that one, gentlemen." He was the only one in the group who customarily addressed his companions as *gentlemen*. The others would have said *boys*.

"Sure," Bill Zanias told them, "I get it that one."

"For God's sake." French tugged at his shirt collar again. "Sit down, Bill."

"I'm alone," Bill explained. "Thank you. Got to wait on customer."

Ralph Togland broke the sugar-bowl top in two pieces. They all looked at it, but no one said anything.

L. T. Hyatt reached into his pocket, brought out a new package of Camels, and shook loose a cigarette. "Bill, how would you Greeks like to see the bank reopen?"

"Sure," said Bill. "We like to see it open, because it is bad to have to get money from Philadelphia. It is bad almost two weeks, ever since the banks close."

"Of course it is," said L. T. He and French nodded in studied agreement. "It's bad for the whole town, Bill, if you understand what I mean. The worst thing that can happen is for a community to lose confidence in itself."

Togland pushed the two parts of the sugar-bowl cover back together, and squeezed them until there was only a ragged line to show the break. "He won't get that one."

"Sure I get it," said Bill. "I guess you are right when you say it is bad for towns to have a banks close."

"Bill's no fool," said Sterling French kindly. "Are you, Bill?"

Zanias shook his head.

Ralph Togland asked, as if he did not already have the figures carefully typed on a sheet of paper in his breast pocket, "Bill, how much did you have in your account ten days ago?"

"I guess maybe I have about eighteen thousand dollars."

"And how much did Tommy have?"

Bill shrugged.

"You mean you don't know, Zanias? You don't know how much Tommy had?" Togland's native testiness was in his voice now.

Bill shrugged again. "I guess Tommy, he has got a lot of money in the banks."

"What Ralph means," said Sterling French, "is that Tommy had the bulk of the money that you boys have got, in his name."

"Sure. I guess maybe you know all about that, Mr. French."

L. T. Hyatt said, "Their cousin Andrew's got a separate account, too."

Bill Zanias's eyes were smaller and darker, when L. T. talked of Andrew. "Andrew is back in Greece," he said. "He is back in Návplion. In Argolis. Maybe you remember about that, Mr. Togland and Mr. French?"

Sterling French's face was pink. "Of course. Andrew's been visiting quite a while, hasn't he?"

"I get cablegrams from Andrew last week," Bill told them. "I get two. The week before that I get also a cablegrams."

"Well." L. T. lit the cigarette which had been pasted, dry and unlighted, between his lips. "That's neither here nor there. The point is this, Bill: there's such a thing as the waiver system. W–a–i–v–e–r."

"It means to waive something," whispered Ralph Togland as in confidence.

"That's it, Bill. To waive—to put aside. Now, when a bank's closed, people can't get their money out until it opens up, can they? Of course not." He answered his own question again. "Of course they can't, Bill. Now, we all want to see the bank reopen. I mean, we want—to see—the bank—opened up again. Don't we?"

"Sure," whispered Bill Zanias.

"That's right. Now, the only way that the bank can open up is for people to go slow—I mean, take it easy. You see, everybody's sort of nervous and scared because the bank closed. If the bank opened up—say, tomorrow—people might still be so scared that they'd all go down and draw out their money. And then the bank would have to close *again*. Maybe it would close *for good*, and nobody would get any money. Not ever."

"Excuse me," said Bill. He trotted to the cash register on the cigar counter. He rang up the change which the boy in coveralls offered in payment for his snack. Bill said, "Goodbye come again," and returned to the group at the rear table.

Ralph Togland muttered to French, "You try a while."

"O.K.," said Sterling French. "Bill, all banks have to be regulated by the State banking department. If a bank is closed, it can reopen only after permission has been granted. They will grant permission to our institution to reopen its doors, provided that eighty per cent of the depositors agree not to draw out all their money at once. You follow me, don't you?"

"What?" asked Zanias.

Togland swore.

"You understand what I mean, don't you?"

"Sure." Bill planted his hands on his hips and put his feet a little farther apart. "You have to get eighty peoples to say they not draw out their money."

"Not eighty people. Eighty *per cent.* That is, not in numbers, but in amount of deposits. It must be made certain that eighty dollars out of every hundred will not be immediately withdrawn."

Bill nodded. He closed his eyes, then opened them again.

L. T. Hyatt said crisply, "Bill, you've got power of attorney."

"What?"

"You can sign things for Tommy and Andrew. Sign papers, I mean. Well—" He brought out the printed waiver form, from inside his coat. "You just put your John Hancock on this, and everything will be fine."

Bill reached his hand for the waiver, but instead Ralph Togland took it quickly. Togland pretended to be reading the small type . . . he acted as if he had found something not quite acceptable . . . and then again, as if it had been explained to his satisfaction.

He looked up squarely into Bill's eyes without smiling. Possibly in this moment he realized that his face was more commanding of respect and trust when he did not smile.

"It's all right, Zanias. If you sign this little paper, at nine o'clock of the first day the bank reopens you can have ten per cent of your money, if you need it. That is, ten dollars for every hundred—"

"One hundreds for every thousand."

Bill nodded. "Sure, I know all about tens per cent. It was tens per cent money due in Eagle Falls, the day before the banks does not open."

Ralph Togland asked, "What in hell is he talking about?"

"Twenty-two hundred dollars," said Bill Zanias. "There was twenty-two hundred dollars to send to Eagle Falls for mortgage on drive-in."

Sterling French felt of his collar again.

'Then Andrew is in Návplion. He send cablegrams, and say send three thousand dollars. He needs it for his folks. They have not got no money. He says to send him three thousand." Bill added softly, "Mr. French," but French couldn't lift his eyes.

"I go in the banks," Bill continued. "I say to Mr. French now to send money to Andrew, and now to pay tens per cent that is due in Eagle Falls. We buy big mortgage there, and this tens per cent money got to be paid. And you say, Sure, you send."

Simultaneously, Ralph Togland exclaimed. "Look here!" and L. T. Hyatt cried, "But, Bill—"

"That is just before the banks not open again. The County Commercial Savings Banks not open the next morning, and everybody stand around and say, What the hell. But I think anyway, It is lucky I send Andrew the money to Greece yesterday. And Tommy tell me it is lucky we pay twenty-two hundred to Eagle Falls because now we don't worry much—

and after while the banks open up, and we get our other money. But then I get cablegrams from Andrew and he want to know about the three thousand dollars. And my cousin Spyros telephone from Eagle Falls and he say, Where in hell is the twenty-two hundred which Mr. French he does not send? You do not send that mortgage money, Mr. French. You do not send to Andrew his three thousand dollars. Maybe you do not send it because you know the banks not open up, and maybe you want to save your own money."

His voice had grown softer and more apologetic all the time.

L. T. Hyatt said, "Listen, Bill. I don't deny that we made a slip. But things were looking bad, and we were pretty rattled that day. Hell was popping, Bill! You can't hold that against us. We've been friends a long time, and—"

"You want your money, don't you?" cried Togland.

"Sure."

"Well, sign that paper, then!" the banker yelled.

In silence Bill Zanias examined the waiver slip. He read it slowly and painfully, his lips shaping each word, and you could tell when he skipped the difficult ones. . . .

"It says tens per cent. . . ."

"That's it," French muttered, his gaze on the table. "You can get ten per cent if you want to, Bill. All of you boys can—the first moment the bank is open."

"Then six months—"

"That's right. In six months you can get another ten per cent."

"Then six months again—"

L. T. told him, "If everybody plays pool with us, we'll be able to pay off a damn sight sooner than that, and you know it."

"I think I do not sign."

Togland started to jump to his feet, but Hyatt grabbed his arm. "You've got to sign, Bill."

"Why?" inquired Zanias. "Who will make me sign?"

"Everybody will," Ralph Togland cried. "Popular opinion will!"

"You want the good will of people around here, don't you?" asked Sterling French. "Of course you want it. You need it in your business. You couldn't continue in business without it. And if the bank doesn't reopen, you Greeks will never get a cent of your money."

Bill backed off and sat down on a stool by the counter. He smiled shyly. "But maybe other people sign. Maybe you make other people sign. Maybe you get eighty per cent other people, and maybe then the banks open up. And if I do not sign, then maybe Tommy and Andrew and me will take out all our money, and take it up to Mr. Aintree's bank."

"You'll never get a dime," snarled Togland. "You'll never get a dime if you don't sign that paper! The bank won't open."

Bill swung half round on his stool. "Oh, I guess maybe you want the banks to open pretty bad. I guess maybe you get eighty per cent other peoples. Then we will take out our money. *All* our money. We take it out, and go somewhere where folks do not lie and say, Yes, we have send money to Andrew, and have send money to pay mortgage in Eagle Falls."

A milky dampness showed along Togland's wide mouth. For a moment it seemed as if he couldn't get up from his seat.

Sterling French was the first to arise. "All right, Bill, if that's what you say." He picked up his hat and started toward the door. Togland followed. Then, after another moment, L. T. Hyatt got up and went after them.

Bill Zanias walked back behind the counter. He kept pace with the others all the way toward the front door.

L. T. stopped opposite the cash register. He rang his fingernails against its top. "Bill," he murmured reprovingly, "don't you realize that this might be the beginning of the end for you, here in town? You boys do a mighty big business every noon and every night, and you've been in business for a long time. But people will stand for only so much. For your own good, I'm asking you to sign that waiver."

"I think I not sign."

Ralph Togland turned his white face toward Bill, but Sterling French was already outside the door. "By God, I begin to think that there ought

to be a Ku-Klux-Klan around here, or something. There's plenty people will never eat in this lousy dump again! They'll go to a restaurant run by *Americans!*"

Bill blinked his eyes rapidly. He motioned for Togland and Hyatt to stand where they were. "Stay," he told them curtly.

He bent down and began to turn the combination of a small safe beneath the counter . . . when the safe was open, Bill drew out a rectangular document framed neatly under glass.

He slid this across the cigar counter. "I like it," he said, with a certain hypnotic assurance.

Even in defeat and helpless rage, the two men were under his spell. They yielded, they leaned forward to read.

. . . Intends to reside permanently in the United States (when so required by the Naturalization Laws of the United States), had in all other respects complied with the applicable provisions of such naturalization laws, and was entitled to be admitted to citizenship, thereupon ordered that such person be and (s)he was admitted as a citizen of the United States of America.

Bill said, "You did not choose to come to Hamilton County. You were born here. But Tommy and Andrew and me, we choose."

The Desperate Dangerous Smile of Mr. Trask

*A*ll in one morning, said Mr. Louis Trask. In a single Monday morning. So incredible the wonders.

He was near stupidity and he walked seeing all about him, seeing nothing, knowing thin warm yellow of the sun, trying to draw deep breaths, drawing only shuddering shallow ones.

He had come air-footed down Vine Street, walking some seeming distance above the sidewalk. Twice he observed himself amid the reflection of shop windows, and each time he did not at first recognize himself, and wondered who that man might be— man in gray suit and with the brown-and-blue bow tie, thin lucky man with heavy-rimmed glasses and tan felt hat.

The sun, still early but riding high above southeast buildings, beamed down and struck glass and dust of a wide window. Glass and dust built a new mirror here as competently as silvering could have done, and Louis Trask found himself reflected once more.

He halted in his trance, he gazed.

But I should smile.

The spiritual reminder came quivering.

I'm pale, I'm drawn. The great sad world is needing any correction I can give. O charity and benefit and truth . . . and God, dear God . . . I thank you.

He had no more words than he had necklaces. At the Gor-May Groceries & Meats they did not deal in gems or platinum. They dealt in potted shrimps, cocktail crackers, cocktail sausages, and a great many other tidbits and large bits, as Mr. Trask had dealt in them through years when he owned and managed—with the help of Ida—his own store far down on Fourth Street.

Yet the dream and the notion persisted, hidden behind tinned soups and crisp envelopes of dehydrated delicacies in his soul—a savory treasure which now he felt the desire to offer to his Creator and to suffering people who walked their world around him. Fashioned by the same Hand they were . . . he pitied them, knew them as brothers and sisters in a fresh informal religion of generosity.

It began with the buzzer in a third floor hallway some two hours earlier, when Mr. Trask was shaving above the lavatory basin in his small side room. On each floor there was a buzzer controlled by buttons in the front hall downstairs.

Louis Trask listened. One buzz: that would be Miss Burnquist in the front-left. She was a pretty red-haired girl with fat legs and a quiet voice, who clipped and filed and buffered the fingernails of customers in a hotel barber shop.

No, two buzzes, indicating a summons for old Mr. Elam in the front-right. He was an elderly bartender who still worked two nights a week in a downtown cafe. The rest of his conscious hours were devoted to the construction of a pencil-smudged manuscript entitled *From The Other Side of The Mahogany. My Life While Serving Gentlemen and Others in New York, Baltimore and Cincinnati.*

. . . Three, but three. Miss Shirlee DuMode insisted that she was a nightclub singer, and proved it by throaty exercises as she sauntered about her quarters next to Mr. Trask's room. No one knew just where Miss DuMode sang, professionally, but she always paid her rent promptly. Three blares of the buzzer summoned her to the telephone on frequent occasions.

Four! Not three for Miss DuMode, but four for Louis Trask himself.

He listened and stared, razor frozen in his thin hand.

There it was again, growling outside. Four blasts.

Maybe his daughter Martha had sent a Special Delivery letter about—

The buzzer announced callers, telegrams, Specials, telephone calls. Seldom did Mr. Trask receive any of these; therefore he suffered panic as he wiped the lather from his face and put on a bathrobe of Air Force blue. This garment had been deeded him by his son-in-law, M/Sgt. Glen Inkster. Braided piping had frayed into fuzz, but Mr. Trask wore the robe with pride.

In loose slippers, the long fabric held up as a duchess might have carried her train, Mr. Trask progressed down the stairway. From the second floor he peered with caution over a polished banister, for he was in no sartorial condition to receive visitors. Creditors? He had none. Dear friends? He owned a few, but none of these might come calling at this hour of the morning.

He beheld the fat hairy face of his landlady, Mrs. Sylvia Remo. She stood at the foot of the bottom stairway, waiting for him, and she held a yellow envelope in her hand. Louis Trask froze.

"Good morning, Mr. T. I got a telegram for you."

"Oh, thanks."

He died many deaths (other than the factual death which he feared was facing him) as he went down the last flight of stairs. Do not let it be Martha. Not sick or— Do not let it be Glen. Away off overseas, flying, and then maybe Martha gets a telegram from the Air Force, and then— She has to send one to me—

The kids. Do not let it be little Mattie or Inky. Inky I have never seen, because he is only seven months old and—

A fall, a tumble out of the window? Leukemia? A—a fire at their house? Do not let anything happen to Inky until I can take my vacation in August and go down there and see him. Probably my last vacation. I have held a granddaughter in my arms, never a grandson. . . .

The last four steps, his hand stretching down, Mrs. Remo's arm straining up, the dangerous telegram close. . . . And let me live, make Dr. Dilstein let me live, no matter what report he gets from that laboratory, make Dr. Dilstein let me live long enough to go to Tampa and—

Mrs. Remo swam away, and the hall was waiting and spectral, full of voices ready to screech but not screeching yet, and the tearing of the yellow envelope made a great noise in a universe unbearably silent.

HOORAY GLEN ARRIVED HOME LAST NIGHT LOOKS WONDERFUL KNEW YOU'D WANT TO KNOW. LOVE MARTHA

Mr. Trask spread his bony legs apart and sat upon the trodden carpet of the stairway. The robe fell away inelegantly and for a time he looked like a disreputable cartoon of a forgotten Gandhi. Then he got up and started slowly to climb.

He had never owned a son, except for a twisted wad of too-young flesh which he pitied for a moment, back in 1941.

"Trask, I'm sorry. Sorry the poor little fellow couldn't make it. Only six months—"

That had been his son, until Sgt. Inkster came along and married Martha. Broad-faced, quiet-spoken, wide-beamed Glen.

"You know what Colonel Ellis told Glen the other day, Daddy? Well, Glen won't tell you, so I'll tell you."

"Oh, shut up, hon."

"Daddy, the Colonel said to him, 'Inkster, you did a swell job on this trip. You're just about the best flight engineer I've ever flown with, and I've flown with plenty.'"

And now Glen was back; the perils were behind him once more, and probably behind him forever. He was a veteran of three wars, and a veteran of all sorts of training dangers in between. He might never have to serve abroad again. Mr. Trask prayed that Glen would not, and tears came, and the telephone was braying in the hall beneath.

Louis Trask had no handkerchief with him, so he was compelled to wipe his eyes on the tough woollen sleeve of the bathrobe. He was not through drying his eye-sockets, and his wet glance searched for dark steps of the next stairway, when Mrs. Remo's voice rose and pierced him.

"Mr. T., you got back to the third floor yet? Telephone."

He chuckled out some remark about exercise . . . if this kept up he'd be getting quite a workout, like a fellow playing golf or something.

. . . Rubber-textured covering of the front corridor, the telephone upon the shelf, the Remo door closing politely at the end of the hall.

"Hello."

"Mr. Trask? This is Dr. Dilstein's office. One moment, please."

. . . All the dreadful things which you must tell other people, and have told them before, with the necessary cruel kindness of one who deals in degeneration of the human body . . . verdict relayed from that distant laboratory which had my tissue. . . . Go ahead, tell me. I'm just ordinary, a widower, lonely, I love Martha and Glen and the kids but they're all I've got— Ida's gone, she died seven years ago, you remember. Go ahead. I knew it all the time and I'll try to be brave. Just a—a grocery store clerk, nowadays—but— Tell me, and give me the final word, and I'll try—

"Morning, Mr. Trask. Dr. Dilstein. I stopped by my office early, before leaving for the hospital. Some messages came in Saturday, and I thought you'd want to know. That report from—"

The laugh, the laugh. Oh, how could—?

"I've got some pretty good news for you."

News. Got news—

"The pathologists have checked thoroughly. You haven't a thing to worry about. It's what we call benign—

"—Yes, absolutely O.K. We can snip that out, any time. It'll scarcely lay you up at all. No hurry about it. Just at your convenience."

Mr. Trask stood aloof and listened to his own mild voice. "Thanks, Dr. Dilstein. Thanks a lot. You sure gave me some good news. Like you—said. I sure do appreciate your calling. You know how I'm— I mean, how I been feeling. Kind of worrying. I was remembering—thinking about—about Mrs. Trask and how— I sure do appreciate your calling—"

His voice broke apart, he went away and left the receiver off the hook, he remembered, he trembled back to replace it. He searched through hissing hollows for the stairs.

Again the warm loose voice of Mrs. Remo. Poor tired woman, and how hard she worked, and relatives always on her neck. Mr. Remo was a short-order cook, but he didn't earn a lot; and those three girls had every one of them married a louse or a weakling.

The landlady's big face was forced through the opening, her dark chins sagging on the soiled gingham of her arm as she held her apartment door ajar.

"You're sure the popular guy today, Mr. T. Calls and wires and stuff. Say, there was something I wanted to tell you. You heard about Aunt Gracie?"

Aunt Gracie was a sullen indigent creature addicted to gallons of cheap red wine. She had been living off the Remo bounty for nearly a year. Mr. Trask loathed her because she never spoke to her niece except with a snarl or an inebriate's sob. He had tried not to resent her for another more selfish reason: when Aunt Gracie came, he was moved out of his pleasant rear-east room on the second floor, and exiled to that bleak side-cell upstairs.

Mr. Trask had rejoiced in that rear-east room after he gave up the old apartment on Elm Street and came to dwell with the Remos on Vine. The room had two windows instead of one, it looked out on a garden of sorts, in summer it was so pleasant, with breezes and whistle-throbs finding their way up from the river.

And the cat. A big gray tomcat haunted the dirty garden court at times. Louis Trask had often seen him sitting on the fence, and at last he made advances. The tomcat seemed interested in considering a friendship. One lonely evening Louis armed himself with salmon and condensed milk, and dug a dusty plank out of rubble in the basement.

This plank was long enough to reach from the fence-top to a window ledge, and up the gangway the cat came marching in time, to sample Mr. Trask's bounty, to allow his back to be stroked and his little washboard rubbed beneath the warm fur of his neck. It was the beginning of a contented if sporadic relationship. Mutt (it was Louis's name for Puss; he did not know the true one) must belong to someone in the neighborhood . . . he wore a red collar.

But he visited Louis Trask amiably, and brought the profit of softness and purring. A nail held the board in place—until Aunt Gracie moved in— day and night. Sometimes Mutt spent part of the night on Louis's bed. Louis could reach down and touch him, and hear a growl of purring through the gloom.

"I thought maybe Joe had said something about it. Well, Aunt Gracie's going—"

Mrs. Remo lowered her voice into mystery.

"—To live with Paula in Cleveland. That's my cousin—you know—Mrs. Boretti, her other niece."

His mind was stewing, trying to make sense out of a golden telegram and a silver telephone call and now this jeweled message.

"When's she going?"

"Week after next. You can have that back room on the second floor again if you want to. Course, it's two dollars more than you're paying now."

Throughout baking days of summer, in all stark hot nights, breeze would come up from the river with a texture of satiny dark currents and ancient steamboats about it. Even a distant chiming of carillon bells might be heard, mellow and reassuring.

Light and air and music he would have again. And Mutt—Mutt the cat might be tempted back, if he had not run away or been run over in the meantime.

"Gee, you keep opening your mouth and not saying anything. Mr. T, are you all right? You ain't sick?"

"No, I'm—fine. And— Sure! I sure would like to have that room back, when Aunt Gracie goes. I sure am much obliged, Mrs. Remo."

When he came down again, prepared to walk to his work at August Gorglattner's grocery, mail had arrived. Dreamily he fingered through the little pile. . . . One of those inevitable communications to Mr. Elam from his union . . . two letters for Miss DuMode and both from overseas. She seemed to have a considerable acquaintance among sailors and marines. . . . Mr. Trask didn't expect any mail. There had been a postcard from

Martha several days before, and she didn't write too often. Naturally she was busy with little Mattie and Inky. Sometimes Mr. Trask received a notice about insurance dividends which had accumulated on one of his three small policies. The policies were long since paid up, and he let the dividends —even so tiny—accumulate to. the eventual profit of his grandchildren.

But here was something near the bottom of the pile and looking dangerously official. *Penalty for private use* — A Government envelope, and addressed to him, his name peeked out through a narrow window. It said *Bureau of Internal Revenue* in the upper corner.

He turned toward the door. Mr. Trask had the normal man's dread of such a missive. It was all a pain, a threat, a signal of implacable bureaucratic dictation. Sometimes he tried to lecture himself, to remind himself of the urgency of maintaining the Government in force. Income taxes must represent a promise and security for children in their unexplored future.

Still, it was difficult to consider this letter as anything except a grenade which would explode and wound him the moment he opened it.

He cried without speaking (he did indeed make a sound, a grunt or moan) as he stepped into the street, "—Can't bother me today. Not today! No, they sure can't. I don't care how

much they say I owe them. I'll dig up the cash—pay them so much a week, if necessary. And I've got money in the bank, in Christmas savings. Can't get that out until the end of the year, but— Anyway, I don't care. Not after what Dr. Dilstein just said. And knowing Glen is home safe, and— They can't bother me today!"

He stopped beside a railing, took off his glasses, rubbed them with care, put them on again. He tore open the grenade.

Here was a long stiff wafer; a flimsier paper was attached, with a lot of smudged carboned figures.

Louis Trask studied the numerals. Two hundred and forty-three dollars and sixty-two cents. A *refund* for an overpayment on his 1967 tax.

That was the big year, four years after Ida died, when finally he sold his store. He had shown the profit, as guided by a fifty-dollar consultant. It appeared belatedly that the consultant had made a mistake in the Government's favor. This queer bluish stiff paper was a check. It looked like a bond or something. Two hundred and—

Louis Trask moved blankly up Vine Street. He thought of pinching himself, he dared not pinch. He would not die of a wicked growth, as Ida had done—not now at least. His beloved daughter's beloved Glen had been plucked from destruction and jeopardies of Viet Nam. Louis could live in the rear-east-second-floor again. He had this money—an endowment, a gift, a prize, a buried hoard.

He could not weep now, he was past weeping.

Mr. August Gorglattner's polished rosy face shone toward Louis Trask above a stack of egg-crates.

"Pop said—"

Miss May Gorglattner, the proprietor's daughter, nodded severely and importantly above the cash register.

"—Pop said he wanted to see you right away, soon as you came in. There he is, out back—"

Louis Trask walked more slowly than he might have walked the day before. His glance went up to the gaily-painted Bavarian clock over gleaming refrigerators. He was all of twelve minutes late. But Gorglattner was kindly to his employees, and surely—

"Morning, Louis."

"Morning, Mr. Gor. I didn't realize I was so late. I had—had some things come up and—"

The burly proprietor glanced carelessly at the watch strapped across his red hairy wrist.

"Oh, I didn't notice. I want to talk to you about something. Come on—"

He led the way past mountains of cartons, through the rear room and into a well-swept court. He was one of the mildest and most honest men alive—so mild and so honest that you would think he might never make a fortune. Yet he had, he had—a small one.

"Look. Louis. You know I like to fish."

Mr. Trask nodded dumbly. He thought of the shining glass fly-rod which May bought for her father's Christmas, and had displayed secretly to all before she wrapped it up. "That new rod. I guess you ain't had a chance to use it yet. What's it for—trout?" Mr. Trask knew little about fishing.

"Sure, trout, salmon, all kinds of stuff. Look, you remember my brother Paul? He was here from Canada last winter."

A spear of sunlight found its way between buildings, and burned into the tiny court, and the spear was beautiful.

"See, it's away to hell-an-gone in the mountains, up in Alberta. But Paul can't get loose till August . . . trailer, and then maybe we'd go by canoe or on horseback . . . realize you always have your vacation in August, but if it wouldn't throw too big a wrench in your machinery . . . only one I can really trust to be in charge while I'm gone. May doesn't understand enough about stocking, especially perishables."

The words wrapped Mr. Trask,

touched him, draped him, fell around him, lay unbreathing.

. . . Not to wait until August, but to start his vacation "as soon as possible." The others would have to be staggered in between: vacations for May, for Ryan the deliveryman, for old Holstrup—

The bulbous blue eyes of Mr. Gor regarded him pleadingly. "Look, what I'd do, Louis. If you are willing to start right away, I'll make it three weeks vacation for you, with pay, instead of two. Then I can go for all of August with a clear conscience. Knowing you'll be here."

"Sure."

"It's asking a lot, asking you to change your plans. But if you can see your way clear—"

"That'll be O.K., Mr. Gor."

"Louis, it's a load off my mind. When will you leave?"

"This is—Monday. Be all right if I start—today, Mr. Gor? I mean— I could start now. *Right now.*"

The grocer began one of his slow rare grins, but he was regarding Mr. Trask with some amazement. Mr. Trask felt his hand trapped momentarily within his employer's great clean mealy hand. Then he turned, settled his neat hat on his neat bald head, and found himself walking, and saw the green twin spires of a hilltop church, and accounted them to be perfection.

Twice daily, sometimes oftener, he had passed that colorful poster swabbed against a billboard. *Budget Air Transport Co.,* flamed the words at the bottom. *Vacation in Peaceful Florida!* flamed the injunction at the top. *A Happy Pleasureland Winter and Summer. Fly with Comfort and Safety in Luxury Jet Sky Coach . . . Tampa. $77.77 round trip incl. tax and FIFTY THOUSAND DOLLARS INSURANCE.* Seventy-seven dollars and seventy-seven cents. Of course it might cost a couple of dollars to ride out to the airport in a bus. But Martha and Glen could meet him in Tampa in that imported sports-type car of which they were so proud.

. . . and don't forget, Dad, that we have got a new studio couch in the living room and it opens into a full-size bed. It will be all ready for a guest any time and I mean a guest from Ohio! Mattie points to that toy piano you sent Xmas whenever somebody is here and I ask her who it was from—to tell people. And she is so proud. People ask her did Santy give it to her, and she shakes her head and her eyes just shine. She says GAMP!

In vision he saw Martha and Glen waiting at the Tampa airport with the children, and little Mattie would be so excited—she would be jumping up and down. He saw the long line of passengers stringing from a Luxury Jet Sky Coach, as he had seen them in fact a few times in his life, although he had never flown. His lone trip to Tampa was effected on a train, sitting up all night, with an invalid woman making noises next to him.

But by grace of the Budget Air Transport Company he might be in Tampa only a few hours after he left home, his suitcase crammed with all sorts of nice things. Not many clothes; he wouldn't need many clothes; he could water the Inkster lawn in an old sweat-shirt and khaki trousers; he would wear his gray suit on the plane. . . .

Seventy-seven-seventy-seven. How much did that leave out of two-hundred - and - forty - three - sixty - two? Plenty, plenty. A new pipe for Glen— no, *two* new pipes. And bottles of perfume and stuff for Martha. Nylon stockings . . . she was so pretty and feminine, she just went crazy over girl-stuff, always had. And Mattie and Inky—

Games, dolls, animals, birds, monsters. He wouldn't have much other baggage, the airplane people would probably let him carry extra parcels. Maybe a great big silky dog or a lion for Inky. And dolls and—

Another weird picture also obtruded in his dream, though seriously he tried to look away from it. From time to time there were those gloomy ragged photos in papers and magazines. *Government Officials Examine Wreckage of Air Liner at Scene of Crash.* Well, it was a new hazard of existence . . . many of the old hazards had been ruled out . . . there were swift unaccustomed perils.

But suppose something did go wrong? Suppose the Luxury Jet burned in a Kentucky field or plunged into a Georgia forest? Dr. Dilstein had handed his life back to him. Louis Trask wasn't an old man yet, but nobody in his right mind planned to live forever.

"Glen. Here it is. The letter from the air line."

No, from the lawyer. From the insurance company.

"Yes, that's actually it. The whole thing. Fifty thousand dollars. We're named as joint trustees. It's all for the kids."

Dead or alive—win, lose, or draw. *Now I must smile.*

First he smiled at a sickly boy of four or five, and the boy fled from Mr. Trask.

This was at the edge of Inwood Park's cool precinct. The little boy pattered away on his sandals, striped blazer fluttering as he ran. His nurse, a plump woman with porcelain skin and teeth, awaited the child on a bench, beckoning sternly.

"Perry, now you come on."

Louis Trask caught the boy's nasal complaining wail. "Elsa. That man smiled at me—"

Nurse Elsa dragged at Perry's arm, and flung the child behind her. She gave Louis the glare of a pink-eyed mother poodle whose puppies are threatened.

Momentarily all gladness was wiped from Mr. Trask's face as he continued walking, not looking back at the boy and the woman, not listening to the distorted admonition which she must be giving. Ah, he thought, the world was vicious to some. He had a guilty recollection of his own caution, spilled out incessantly to Martha when she used to roller-skate unsupervised along a crowded sidewalk. . . . Strange men, men who offer candy, men who try to talk, men who smile. Don't ever—

He met another woman, and she was alone. Louis Trask guessed that you'd call her an old maid . . . her face was forty, her staring eyes were fifty . . . her face and eyes had left her slim body a generation behind. No matter how prettily she was clad (her mini-skirted suit looked expensive) he felt that she would be a painful customer if ever she walked into the Gor-May Groceries & Meats. Her breed he knew well, had known them all his adult life. The squeezed tomatoes, the bruised fruit, fussy specifi-cations about cheese or paté, the squawk on the telephone when it came to paying.

Nevertheless she was mortal, she was a part of a glorious pageant—a blood cousin, whether he wished to claim her or no.

Accordingly his smile spread wide and unmistakable, thrusting ahead of him as he walked. It brought heat into the woman's face, it brought a gasp from her throat.

Well! was all he heard her say. He felt his own complexion warming, he knew that tiny muscles pulled at his grin, drawing it into bleak rigidity.

For a time there was mist. He must have walked more slowly, must have walked for a block, observing only shapes which he met, not witnessing or evaluating their faces. Too many stiff and lonesome folks in the world, too much suspicion, too much dread. . . .

"Hey, Mr.—"

Quickly Louis Trask glanced to the right. A pearl-gray car had glided to a halt beside the curb, a policeman was beckoning.

He thought for a moment that it must be Patrolman Edson or Patrolman Krensky. They worked in the District where the store was located, and often sauntered inside. Edson was on duty there the day they had the fire in the back room; and Krensky used to have dates with May

Gorglattner before he got married.

But this was a cop he didn't know from Adam.

"Like to talk to you a minute, sir."

The officer was square-faced, pale-eyed. It seemed that (though so young) he owned a secret profound wisdom which most men of middle age never acquire.

"That lady. Know her?"

"What lady?"

Silently the policeman pointed. Louis peered down Vine Street in the direction indicated. He saw a far figure in a mini-skirt, it was the Old Maid, she had crossed to the opposite side of the street and was walking slowly, but looking back over her shoulder.

"Did you make a pass at her?"

"A pass. Did I—"

Monstrous knowledge assailed him. For a moment he could not speak. Instantly he realized it all: nervous woman spotting the police car, skipping across the street, telling— The car making a U-turn, halting him.

His voice was raw.

"Guess I'll never smile at anybody again! First one was a little kid, and he was scared too. He ran to his nurse and—"

"Why were you smiling?"

Sun lay warm against his cheek, and that was good because his cheeks and his entire body felt drained of blood.

(Louis Trask, are you not old and tired?)

He gave his name, and mentioned the Gor-May Groceries, and mentioned also Patrolmen Edson and Krensky in their District. He talked of Glen, and the telegram from Martha, and Dr. Dilstein's call; he mentioned his unprophesied vacation, and also the check from the Bureau of Internal Revenue. He didn't say anything about Mrs. Remo and the rear-east room, for then he'd have had to explain about the tomcat and Aunt Gracie and—

Shield 949 grunted behind the steering wheel. "Psycho. A pure nut."

"Who? Me or her?"

"*Her,* for God's sake!" The policeman philosophized to Louis Trask and to the world at large. "Just imagine what a state our civilization has gotten into! When a man who is happy can't smile at anybody without people wanting to make a job out of it for the cops—"

Louis Trask gazed dourly down at the seal of the city emblazoned in gold on the car's side. "I'm going to quit smiling at *anybody*. Just go down to Tampa—maybe tomorrow, if I can get a ticket—and surprise my daughter and grandchildren. *Then* I guess I can smile. *They* won't call the police."

"Don't you do that, Mr. Trask. You just keep smiling. I figure there aren't enough smiles to go around. You worked in our job awhile, you'd find out." The patrolman nodded. "I've got to get some mileage on this beat car. So long, Mr. Trask."

"So long."

The car began to move. Louis Trask started on south as well. The officer waved at him. "Keep smiling," came his final command, so Mr. Trask tried to obey.

It was a rodent's face, ugly-lipped. You thought you could see fangs within the mouth; yet the lips were closed tightly, and you knew you had only guessed at fangs.

. . . Here was a sneak, a currier for favor, a liar, a cruel character to be walking abroad. Fatty Bondik had looked like that (with a shock Louis Trask realized that Fatty Bondik had left his life more than forty years ago . . . he remembered the dog which Fatty dropped into a sewer hole, the kittens he hurled into an air shaft).

Ogre or not, this young man in a soiled pink-patterned sports shirt was challenging joy and generosity. Louis must not fail, no matter how little he liked the fellow's looks.

I must smile.

"Hey, Doc."

Down the pleasant incline of the street new challenges awaited Louis Trask. But the words arrested him,

as they were meant to do, so he halted and turned.

The sports shirt flared toward him.

"You look like a good guy—"

Mr. Trask supposed with humility that he was a good guy—at least people usually liked him. No one except a staggering drunk might ever wish to give him battle.

He did not enjoy having the rodent's face shoved up so intimately toward his own.

"Doc—"

He was no doctor—maybe it was the glasses—

"See, I had a little hard luck. I haven't got any dough, see? But I got something here. Step over next this doorway."

The hand was on his sleeve, and Louis had either to resist or move toward the empty doorway, so he moved. The young man's other hand slid from the side pocket of his slacks, and Mr. Trask saw with aversion that the cloth around the pocket was soiled.

A wristwatch dangled before his eyes. A silver watch on a linked silver band.

"I got to get some money to get back to Akron, see? This watch is worth a hundred bucks, but I'll let you have it for twenty. On account I need the—"

"Let go of my sleeve."

The man held on. "O.K. Fifteen bucks and it's a deal. You'll never make money that fast in your life again."

The voice was soiled and greasy too. Louis looked into the instantaneous past. He saw dark rooms, hallways strewn with garbage, he heard a termagant's scream and a cop's whistle, it might have been that he heard a sick man coughing and a child sobbing . . . all the same, he knew that he could not re-live the past, nor could he make this person into something better.

His hand was strong. You cannot toil with cartons of canned goods through the years without developing a powerful wrist. He disengaged the clutch on his sleeve. "Where did you steal that watch? What makes you think I'm a sucker? Just because I gave you a smile—"

"Aw—"

Pink Shirt added another word, a nasty word. He darted off speedily, and Louis adjusted his glasses and searched traffic for the glint of a pearl-gray patrol car. He saw none, he saw no policeman on foot. The good Shield 949 had gone to remote distance by this time. And Pink Shirt was vanished quickly.

Louis Trask stood trying to adjust the fresh burden of pain which this new encounter strapped across his shoulders. . . . No, he would not wear the burden. He would let it lie there on the concrete.

He went on south. He smiled at folks who were together, and talking; they did not see Louis, neither did they witness the eagerness he offered. There were people walking alone, preoccupied, insensitive to lumbering traffic on one side and old brick buildings on the other. There were wild little black rowdies, practicing gay mayhem on one another, and only staring suspiciously at this scrawny Evangelist of the Smile if they saw him at all.

. . . Undiluted joy was his to savor. Merely because he had met with miseries, he must not let them infect the clean fare spread before him.

A recollection of his gifts arose to make Louis Trask giddy again. Suppose Glen had not come back safely, suppose Dr. Dilstein had quoted a report which was positive instead of beneficently negative. Suppose—

Thank you, dear God.

And let me laugh with every unknown spirit whom I meet.

The young woman moved toward him slowly; he had seen her ahead, crossing Vine Street with the green light. He must forget the rat which had chewed his sleeve, and lesser hatefulness in the blocks behind (the sullen jowly man who growled over his shoulder and asked Mr. Trask what was so damn funny . . . the crone who had been muttering to herself as she limped by, and who felt Mr. Trask's charm held toward her—who turned, to stand and rant alone when he had passed. Jews and Catholics: she was talking about them).

He would forget the plague of ignorance or dissipation or ailing wits. For this young woman sauntered with the arrogance of youth, and she wore a brief black linen dress and a green scarf, and carried a cheap bright bag swung from her shoulder. Louis Trask reckoned that she was no older than his daughter Martha, though Martha never wore quite that much lipstick.

A scent of heavy perfume came to meet him along with the dark swoop of her velvet gaze.

Earnestly, openly, Louis Trask gave her his smile. He saw a ruddy spark leaping as he warmed it. Then she, the first of all to repay him in kind, was parting her bright lips to show the sparkle. . . .

Four steps he took . . . five.

"What's your hurry—?"

Her voice was smooth behind him.

He stopped quickly . . . *it's been worth all the other disappointments to find one person . . . even if I discover but one.* He beamed, he went to meet her.

"Just taking a walk?"

"Just a little stroll—"

"Not working, or anything? Say, what are you—retired?"

He laughed at the idea. "Gosh, no.

Just happened to start my vacation this morning. Guess I couldn't retire, even if I was rich. Wouldn't know what to do with myself."

He felt a sweep of health and love and opulence. He must share, share . . . tell her about Martha and Glen and the kids, and even about Mutt the gray cat, and Mr. Gor's wanting to go fishing in Canada. . . .

Her eyes had been over and through him. Her assessment was complete, though Mr. Trask didn't realize it.

"You know, you're not *too* old. You're a real sharp-looking guy for your age."

"I just felt so kind of happy and excited that I wanted to tell somebody—"

"You can tell me. Later."

Linen arm, tender flesh behind his sleeve. "If you want to talk, I'll let you talk. We can go over to my place."

"Your place? I—"

"Right off Central Parkway. It's not far. You know, honey, we can have a little drink or something. My name's Hazel. I'll treat you swell. It'll only cost you twenty-five bucks."

He wrenched away, he heard her surprised blasphemy burning the air, vaguely he was aware that the rodent and the hyena snarled alike . . . or whatever animal she was. . . .

Mr. Trask went plunging off, taking unnatural strides, unshed tears stinging him. Shoulders got in his way; people were standing, waiting for a light, he twisted heedlessly through them, tripped against the wheel of a baby carriage, and nearly upset . . . *I'm sorry, I'm sorry* . . . on he went.

Thirteenth Street flowed behind him. Out across Race Street he lunged. Brakes snarled, somebody yelled a frightened insult; he was a damn fool; someone so informed him.

Washington Park. The curb came to meet him, and here was a walk leading toward the bandstand and cannon and monuments beyond. Louis Trask followed it blindly . . . he was weak, he needed to sit. The edge of a bench touched the back of his legs, he crumpled down, his breath gone from him. He lifted an arm grown strangely heavy, and draped his arm along the back of the bench, and turned his face against it. Thus in hiding his face it seemed that he was hiding with permanence the smile which had betrayed him.

The bench exuded a solidity which in itself was a dull benefit. Mr. Trask sat without moving for a very long time—how long, he did not know: perhaps an hour or more. When he tried to shift his left arm he found that the arm had gone to sleep, the nerves were paining him.

People dissolved and departed, other people materialized, the sun stayed steady and high through the century. There'd been tears or happy squealing among children; there'd

sounded gossip which did not affect Louis Trask because he was now remote on a haunted mountain with neither whimsy nor illusion.

Selfish, he described himself, and yet plaintively he knew that the accusation was unfair. What sense in allowing Providence to build a joy for you, if you were reluctant to taste it? Gifts poured in a flood . . . Louis was joyous, counting them . . . he had tried to parcel out a morsel of his satisfaction to humanity, he had not been allowed to do so. Humanity turned aside, or gave him a deaf ear or a clenched fist.

A shape leaned against his knee with comfort of its own. *A child,* thought Louis in his bleak doze, and let his hand stray to explore. He touched thick short hair and encircling leather. A dog had come to sit beside him.

Louis opened his eyes. A large dog indeed, a German shepherd. The nose rubbed cold and moist against his hand, the chestnut eyes regarded him seriously.

"Hi'ya, boy," Mr. Trask whispered.

"His name is Skinner."

The dog's master sat beyond. He was a slim brown-faced bespectacled man of perhaps thirty.

"Hi-ya, Skinner," Mr. Trask whispered again dutifully. In the back of his brain he wondered drearily whether this young colored man would run away or call the police, or try to sell him stolen goods.

"It's a beautiful day, sir."

"Sure is."

Louis blinked at antique bricks of the music hall yonder . . . and the façade of the Hamilton County Memorial building across the way . . . statues of ancient American soldiers and sailors ranked there.

The colored man played lightest music with his voice as he chuckled. "Day like this, a man gets spring fever or summer fever or whatever you want to call it. Man doesn't feel like working."

"Have you been—working?"

"Oh, I called on a client or two this morning. Haven't got any more appointments until one-thirty. Then I've got to see a man over here on Elm. It's very pleasant, just sitting."

Louis glanced at his watch and saw that it was nearly twelve o'clock. He sat more erect, and twisted his stiffened shoulders. The habit of toil and six-day responsibility can be broken with ease only on Sunday, when others of one's own kind are accepting the change. Louis Trask felt guilt, idling on this wood-and-concrete bench, because today was Monday, and he murmured about it. . . . Late . . . almost noon.

"You maybe got some clients of your own to see? Don't tell me we're rivals in the insurance business!"

"No. I work in a store. But I'm on vacation, beginning today."

"Vacation's a very pleasant thing—"

(The colored man declared it to be, although Louis Trask had not found it so except in anticipation.)

"—Unless it's *enforced*."

Once more the tune of the man's gentle laughter. . . . Trask turned to face him squarely, his hand still resting on brindled hair of the dog Skinner.

"You know, you—seem to laugh a lot. Doesn't it ever—" He searched for the most expressive word. "—Backfire?"

The young fellow tilted his head and seemed to be examining the very staring sun itself through black sunglasses.

"I do laugh a lot, I guess. Mr.—?"

"The name is Trask."

"My name is Eastwood. Lenny Eastwood. Mr. Trask, I laugh a lot, because I'm a very happy man. A happy man should laugh, don't you believe? And I'm happy because I'm alive."

He was too young to have worries concerning his own personal Marthas and Glens—far too young to have grandchildren. It was unlikely that he had ever been taunted by that dread of bodily degeneration which had terrified Louis Trask.

"A lot of people, Mr. Eastwood, don't seem to find that enough. I mean, just being alive. They don't even want to smile, unless they think they're going to get something out of it."

"But when you've been near to

death, Mr. Trask! When you've stood within the Valley of the Shadow, and then walked out again, you know what the gift of life really is. My friends—they—"

He had to break off talking for a moment, then he continued. "They didn't make it. They weren't lucky like me. There were five of us. Now the other four are dead, but I'm still here. I've got the gift of life, and so each hour I give thanks."

Again tears stood in Louis's eyes, but these tears did not seem to scorch him, there was no acid or pepper in their quality.

"Where was this? The Valley of the Shadow?"

"On the maps they call it Viet Nam, sir."

"When?"

"Over three years ago. The men who were with me are gone forever. But here I am, and I got my own dear wife and mother and little boy, and I got Skinner. I got my body and soul and I got my life. Being blind doesn't seem to matter at all."

For the first time Louis Trask understood the combined evidence beside him. He realized why Lenny Eastwood might raise his dark face intently toward the sun, black glasses and all; he realized why Skinner wore such a heavy harness with stiff-pronged handle instead of a limp leash.

He sat up and drew heavily on the air, and felt the courage of trees near at hand. Smell of grass and gassy city streets came to his nostrils with pungency.

"Lenny. I mean— You don't mind if I don't say 'Mr. Eastwood.' I'm considerably older than you. Lenny, I'm glad you sat down here on this bench. I've got so much to— Like you, I've got a lot to be thankful for. In a different way. I'd like to tell you about it. You'd really understand."

"Go ahead, sir, if it will do you good. I'm a fine listener. I've learned how to be." He chuckled, and the dog nudged against Lenny's knee.

Louis Trask was thinking aloud. "I wonder . . . sure. The Won Ton Cafe, right over here on Race Street. That's funny: *Race.* . . . Lenny, do you like Chinese food and maybe a glass of beer? Would you care to take lunch with me?"

"I'd be happy to."

Mr. Trask stood up, younger and hardier and purer than he had been when he sat down. Beside Lenny Eastwood, and with the dog marching in stiff harness ahead, Louis Trask walked out of the park, and both men were smiling.

166

A Memory of Miss Hattie

171

A woman sitting by herself in an old rocking chair. . . .

No telling who the woman is or was, and why she sat as she did, or whether she was happy or not, or who her folk were.

But observing her thus, solitary and seemingly abstracted, causes one to think about the many ladies he's seen, lingering alone in their chairs—perhaps on a porch, perhaps just within the window—or maybe sometimes out on the grass under a tree.

Consider the case of Miss Hattie Jaylson. She was an old maid, crippled and frail, and she lived with her aged widowed mother and a niece and nephew-in-law, Mr. and Mrs. Ed Brann, who had several tiny children.

. . . Nowadays this would be termed a matter for investigation by the American Society for Psychical Research; but in our town in those years few people had ever heard of the ASPR. Nor had many folks heard of poltergeists: those noisy and mischievous critters which displace objects, and sometimes smash bottles and dishes, and even large pieces of furniture.

. . . It began in the middle of one dark spring night, with enormous poundings on the outer wall of the house—beatings and thuddings so loud that close neighbors were awakened as well as the family within doors. The Brann children reported that they had been shoved out of their beds by some unseen force, and they wailed about it, and the baby screamed. The whole family crept downstairs in order to escape, and cardboard boxes were flung at them as they retreated. A clock went off its mantelpiece to crashing disintegration, and the china closet toppled on its face, breaking all contents and the glass door as well.

That was just the beginning. At daylight neighbors came in and watched the teakettle sail off the stove, and saw a hammer flung through a window when no one was around to fling it.

Within two days practically every dish in the house had been broken, and a good deal of the furniture too. When old Mrs. Jaylson sent for the Town Marshal, he stood around and shook his head; and then jumped every time something was shattered in the next room or sometimes in the same room.

The family rented this house. They still owned a large farm down in the south end of Hamilton County, but there were tenants living there, farming the land. Mr. Brann had a local plumbing business . . . that was the reason Grandma and the crippled Miss Hattie and the rest of them lived in that rented house.

Alexander Creery owned the place. He came to, see what on earth was going on, and perhaps to catch a malefactor in the act. Alexander Creery didn't own the furniture or the teacups: those belonged to the Jaylsons and the Branns. But he did own the windows, and he was speechless with rage which couldn't be directed toward any living soul, when he stood near a dining-room window, and watched the weighty Bible lift itself off an opposite table and plunge through the glass pane.

Creery was a man of strong opinions, and had always felt himself able to cope with any riddle in life. It was with some satisfaction that his wife reported to her friends, "At last Alexander's got something which he can't explain!"

The one person in town who had read deeply on the subject of psychical research made several calls at the house, and questioned members of the family. He was an earnest Universalist named Reverend Jerome Hissner, and he sat beside Grandma Jaylson and asked her if there had ever been similar occurrences at an earlier date.

"Oh yes."

"When?"

"When we lived on the farm."

"Did similar things occur on many occasions?"

"Oh yes."

The old lady said that it happened more or less in cycles. There wouldn't be any such occurrences maybe for several years in a row. Then, all of a sudden, the disruptive influences were at work, and violently.

"What happened?"

"Just about like now. And gates'd be opened, and the stock'd be let out to ramble all over the neighbors' property. Doors'd open—"

"Locked doors?"

"Yes. Even when they were locked."

"Plates and cups broken?"

"Oh yes. We finally used pie-tins to eat off of, and drank out of tin cups so's they wouldn't get broken."

"Do you have any idea who might be at the bottom of this business—I mean, do you have any notion about what person might be responsible?"

"I think I know."

"Who?"

"Not saying." Then Grandma Jaylson would sigh, and twist her hands in her apron, and go back to rocking silently again.

We children—hastening home from school for our noon meal, as we did in those days—used to stop and gaze with awe at the haunted house. I remember one day there was a sheet hanging out of an upper story window and trailing down the outside clapboards. Kenneth Neel reckoned the sheet was the tail of a ghost, and we thought he was quite a wit for saying that. But none of us would have ventured inside, even had we been permitted to do so. We just looked, and giggled nervously.

The whole Jaylson–Brann tribe had to move out for a while. I don't know where they stayed—maybe with relatives and friends. And I don't remember whether or not the destructive imps accompanied them. I do remember this: that Miss Hattie Jaylson was shipped off a little later on, sent to our State capital to a private sanitarium known as Ord's Retreat. But pretty soon the Ord people sent word that they didn't want Miss Hattie there any longer. Bad things seemed to be happening in Ord's Retreat as well. Bed covers were flying around, and dishes being hurled, and so on. So Miss Hattie was escorted back home on the train. But the family noted that she seemed mysterious about something . . . as if she had a secret, all her own.

There came a day when Grandma Jaylson lay asleep on her bed upstairs, and Mrs. Brann and the little ones were gone away somewhere; and Mr. Brann, the nephew-in-law of Hattie, was busy at his plumbing establishment. He received a telephone call from the man who drove the local taxicab.

"Just thought you ought to know, Ed—"

"What's the matter?"

"Well, your Aunt Hattie just phoned for me to pick her up in my taxi and take her to the afternoon train."

"What?"

"Yes, that's what she wanted. I figured— Well, you know your Aunt Hattie's a little queer, and I thought maybe I ought to tell you—"

"I'll go right home," said Ed Brann. He did, and found Aunt Hattie on the porch. Crippled or not, she had packed her bag and was all ready to go. She had fallen in love—or thought she had—with one of the middle-aged orderlies at Ord's Retreat. I guess the orderly thought she had money, and so he wooed her, and they were planning to run off and get married.

This romance was quashed, and everybody said, "Now watch the new dishes go sailing off the tables over there at the Jaylsons'. And watch the flatirons being tossed through windows!"

. . . Strangely enough, it didn't happen any more. Perhaps the advent of even such an unconsummated love in Miss Hattie's dreary life had caused the demons to cease their evil exertions. . . . Nothing more happened, as far as the rest of the townsfolk knew. Grandma Jaylson died in another year or two: a natural death from complications of old age. Then Miss Hattie was the senior member of the family for a while, and eventually she died.

I encountered her once in her dotage. With two other youths, I had been engaged by town authorities to conduct a school census, compiling a record which would include all young people between the ages of five and twenty-one, along with their names and ages and such vital statistics. We were given ledgers in which to keep these accounts, and in trepidation I carried my ledger up to the front porch of the Jaylson–Brann house. After I'd knocked, Miss Hattie came slowly from the interior, leaning on two canes. Her eyes were narrow and deep-set, the skin of her dried old face seemed made of pebbles or plaster.

"Good afternoon, Miss Jaylson. I'm taking the school census. Are there any children in this family between the ages of five and twenty-one?"

She hung there between her canes, looking down at me through the screen door, and then slowly she sank into a chair and just sat, staring.

I repeated my question. She began to rock. And she stared no longer at me but just into space.

Woman sitting alone. Poor thing . . . rocking and staring. . . . Although it was commonly reported that she could talk intelligently when she was in the mood.

Nothing for me to do but get out of there. I got out, fast.

. . . Years later there came a meeting with the Reverend Mr. Hissner, the Universalist pastor who was then living in another town. We discussed the Jaylson case, and he told me that he was puzzled because there didn't seem to be any nexus. . . . What was a nexus? It was the individual who supplied the power—who was the impulse for activity of peculiar forces in a poltergeistic case.

"Usually it's a person just under the age of puberty—one who has not attained full puberty as yet. More often a female than a male."

"Reverend Hissner, there weren't any people of that age around."

"I know. The eldest child of the Branns wasn't more than seven or so. Funny. . . ."

More years passed, and my own reading and experience expanded, and I became a member of the American Society for Psychical Research, and learned considerably more about poltergeistic phenomena. This led to correspondence with Mr. Harry Price, the famous British investigator. I dug up old newspaper clippings, and had them copied and sent to Harry Price. I suggested a theory: Aunt Hattie Jaylson had never attained a normal puberty. In other words, old as she was, she might serve as the traditional nexus . . . it was the psychic faculty emanating from her which made possible those pointless but destructive occurrences. I put forth this theory rather diffidently, and was astonished when Harry Price informed me that he had come to the same conclusion.

Perhaps he knew of other such cases. Somewhere perhaps in his past, too, there clung the recollection of a strange old maiden lady, sitting alone in a chair, staring into space.

The Wickedness of Bernardine

It's hard to be a child.

Our nice neighbor, Mrs. Banan, was baking cookies, and she gave two cookies to Sandra, and two to Mimi, and two to Linton, and two to me. And Bernardine— One cookie was kind of broken in two, and she gave that to our dog, and Bernie ate it up in one bite.

I ate one of my cookies, and it was so good; but I thought I'd save the other one, and then eat it right in front of everybody else, after theirs were gone, and say, "Ummm! I got a *cookie*," or something like that. Then we all started back down towards home, and I was holding that cookie in my hand. We'd gone part way down the hill, and I felt something wet brushing my hand. I looked down, and the cookie was gone. Bernie had it, and she just swallowed it. She wagged her tail, like she hadn't done anything bad. She just wagged.

I cried. The girls laughed, and told me I oughtn't to cry over one little cookie.

But I couldn't help crying.

It's hard to be a child.

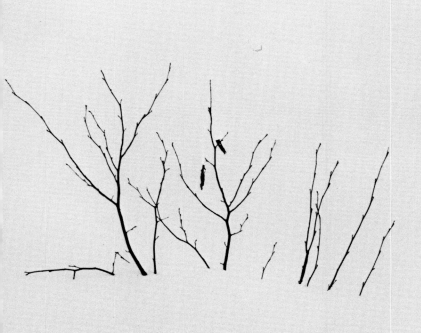

On
My
Honor

*O*ne day, more than sixty years ago, on emerging from kindergarten class, I displayed with pride a brand-new Lincoln penny, the first I had ever seen or owned.

Such coins were just beginning to be circulated in that year, but a fellow kindergartener showed scorn when I exhibited this prize.

"That's nothing," he said. "Murray McMurray's got a whole pocketful of these Lincoln pennies, and he's giving them away to kids."

I didn't have an idea who Murray McMurray might be, but I craved to set eyes upon such a fabulous being. Imagine any man with a pocketful of beautiful copper-shining pennies! And also possessed of such charitable traits! . . .

Accordingly my small friend marched me down to the Hamilton County State Bank, and we peeped at a tall young man officiating at a window of the savings department. He stood raw-boned, big-eared, and with a twinkling enthusiasm about him.

Four years later, in 1913, he became Scoutmaster of the first Boy Scout troop in that town. Today it's one of the oldest troops in the Country.

He presided as Scoutmaster— No, that's not the word: he *strode* as Scoutmaster— For two generations.

*S*ame old hall on the third floor of the South School building . . . has been, all these years. I look at the Scouts sitting rapt, watching the wall-climbing contest. And so many of those boys wear glasses: one, two, three, four, five, six, seven, eight— Nine at least, in the small crowd watching.

(Maybe today's life is harder on boys' eyes than was the life of half a century ago? . . . Yet I rather doubt it. It's probably the mere matter of better care for eyes of the young. All sorts of kids must have needed glasses in the old days, and didn't have them.)

In these slant-ceiled quarters under the building's mansard roof, placards paper the walls. Murray has been gone for a decade now, but who is that vigorous-looking graying man with the long nose and big ears? John McMurray, of course. He took up the job of Scoutmaster when his father relinquished it.

With a reading glass I examine one photograph, and feel a momentary quiver of pride. . . . It was in the year of 1916–17 that they first started keeping track of what came to be known as the Honor Ten.

Hurray. I made the grade.

The evidence looms high on the wall, above the head of the boy who's climbing over. Earl Jacobson was first, Glen Olmstead second. And there I am, third.

We scan the Honor Ten lists for the few years following. My, my . . . Carl Gore won, in the year of 1920–21, and also the following year.

Where is Carl Gore today?

Why, standing right next to that wall, watching the boy climb over. Probably holding a stop-watch, keeping time on the event. Carl's been assistant Scoutmaster for a mighty long while.

This Boy Scout activity is rather habit-forming.

*I*t's an Open Meeting: you can see all those mothers, and little brothers and sisters—and a lot of fathers, too—sitting out beyond.

A certain small boy will watch the contests and the few simple ceremonies, and go home and snuggle into bed. He'll lie awake, possessed by ambition and illusion . . . an ambition which fairly chokes him in the throat, an illusion which is never *de*lusion, but an authentic glimpse into his own shining future.

How long will it be until he, too, becomes a Scout?

How many centuries will he have to wait before he stands in that cavernous room, extending the three middle fingers of his upheld right hand in the Scout sign, and repeating after John McMurray, "On my honor, I will do my best to do my duty to God and my country? . . ."

You,
Dear
Lord,
Will
Under-
stand

*D*ear Lord:

We thank Thee from the bottom of our hearts for letting the Loam family get together this way for another reunion after a space of years.

I believe I'm merely echoing a notion that's in everybody's mind when I offer a report on the Loams, great and small. Of course that takes into consideration the Cardells and Wickeys and Liffs and such, all of whom are with us today because the blood of Elwood and Tabitha Loam runs in their veins.

Aunt Caddy was released from suffering more than six weeks ago. It is needless to say that we miss her, and always will; but also we are proud of the fortitude she displayed throughout her ordeal. Two days before her death she listened to words of honest admiration, spoken both by her doctor and her minister. You know what she uttered in reply? She looked up at them, and smiled, and she says in her weak voice, "Oh, I don't know. Probably it ain't as bad as what Elwood Loam had to endure when he got captured by them Comanches, afore he was rescued."

And you rescued *her,* dear Lord. You surely did.

Clegg and Mabel lost a little boy baby, and we grieve with them accordingly. Flo Cardell lost her dearly betrothed, killed in a plane crash in the Navy. And Grandpa Ab Wickey is mighty sick in a nursing home right now, and they don't reckon he'll ever get up again. But just the same, he's lived to be ninety-two, and was spry as a cat until a couple of years ago.

Now let's look at the bright side of the picture, which is truly the most extensive.

Bill thought he was going to have to pay at least three thousand dollars extra, on his last year's income tax, and what happened? He only had to pay nineteen dollars and twenty-three cents.

Mike is now working on his father's new job—it's to be a beautiful apartment building—so he'll have a nice chunk saved against his next year at the University. Mike's got a mighty cute girl friend, too.

Carol was the hit of the season when she took over a difficult role in a production by the Community Players. She did it on just a few hours notice, but she really— How you say it? She wowed them.

Susan is growing prettier by the minute, and has got more friends than a dog has fleas. She received real good marks in school, too, on her last report card.

Same for Tommy, except he's not growing pretty—he's growing handsome. And he shows the makings of a real cagey quarterback.

Uncle Nick Cardell got throwed by his horse a spell ago, but he refused to be taken to town to the doctor. Nick says, "Hell. First time I got throwed by a horse was the first time I ever *rode* a horse. And that was fifty years ago." You just can't get past Nick, can you? Well, he's here today, sound as sound can be. So we give our thanks for that.

Esther Loam is sporting a diamond solitaire, if you please! She and Keene Finchley plan to tie the knot in two–three more months, just as soon as Keene gets out of that monkey suit he's been wearing for the past three–four years.

Peter Loam enlisted, and is now stationed at Lackland. He's hoping to get into the electronic end of the business. More power to him! As for his sister Marjorie, she's got a fine new secretarial job in Waco, and says she loves every minute of it.

Young Jeff is off to a boy's camp for the second year, and he likes camp so well that I reckon he'll grow up to be one of these counsellors or whatever they call them.

Baby Melissa can drink her fruit juice, holding her cup with her own two little hands. Just saw her do it, a while ago.

We've got representatives living down at the Space Center in Houston: Lonny and Ruth. Lonny did his part in the successful flight of Apollo 11, for which we give praise.

Lydia is really hell on wheels. Never stops trotting or talking when she's awake, and Mamma Ruth reports that they practically have to clobber her over the head, to get her to go to sleep.

Godfrey Wickey lost several head of stock, including a valuable bull calf, which got struck by lightning. But God Wickey isn't complaining a mite. For he was astride his cow pony not more than a hundred yards distant when the bolt came down. No, God considers himself lucky to be here. So do we all.

Aunt Feeb Loam has finally finished with remodeling her house— got the new rooms furnished, and everything. She says it's been *Outgo* all the time, but now for a change it'll be *Income*, since she has four roomers instead of two. And a waiting list, as per usual. Nobody could live more comfortably than they do at Aunt Feeb's.

Bessie had six little girls to a slumber party last week. According to Mother Mandy there wasn't much *slumber* involved. She says she and Lowell got precious few winks of sleep because of the ringing of those "little belles." Lowell said that, when he got out with his Herefords next day, he was tempted to lie down and go to sleep alongside them.

There's a brand new hoist at Arch Liff's filling station, which is a fine thing: he was literally turning customers away. Also he's in the act of closing a deal to renew his lease with the oil company for another three years. Good.

There was a beauty contest for twins at the Fair, and of course Babby and Tabby won *that.* Speaking of the Fair, our old Loam strain really showed up. Lucas took top honors with his stallion, Three Years and Over; Minnie got a blue ribbon for a cockerel and also for her pullets; and young Madeline took a First with her Girl's Pony Under Saddle. And when you

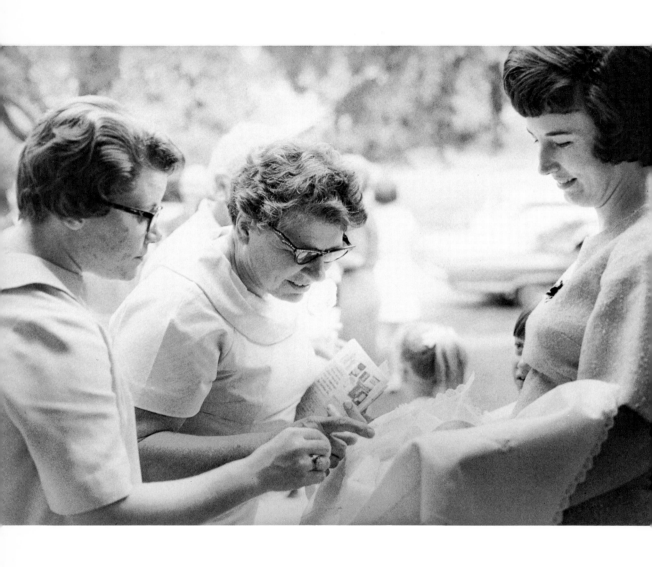

start adding up the prizes our womenfolks gathered in, for crocheting and quilts and jelly and melon-rind pickles— It would take too long to tell You, so I won't try.

Just let me say that the Loam family, with their kin and and branches — We're proud folks, but not overbearingly proud. I guess on the whole we're pretty good neighbors. . . . Oh, we don't love all our neighbors as ourselves, not by a dang sight! There's a few mean people in Hamilton County, just like anywhere else. For some kinds of meanness there's but one language which communicates, and that's a punch in the jaw. Sorry it has to be that way, but You, dear Lord, will understand.

We try to lend a helping hand when and where needed, and we don't go around shouting about it. We try to respect and honor each other, to raise our children to be clean and industrious and able; to offer loyalty to our families, our communities, our County—to the Great State of Texas —and above all, to the United States of America.

When we look out and see our ranges or our wheat, we honor Thee. We thank Thee for Thy blessings, and for the inheritance Thou hast awarded us.

*T*o tell the truth, Lord, I'd never dare to say these things. It wouldn't be fair to take up Your time with all this data about one family, when You've got so many others to look after. These things are in my heart, sure enough, but I'd be too embarrassed to publish them abroad. A lot of the relatives might be embarrassed too.

So let's just say, *The Lord watch between me and thee, when we are absent one from another.*

Joy

I cannot understand everything that He says or that She says, but I do not need to. They know that I have all the love in the world, and then some, to give; and They are eager to accept it. That makes me feel like loving Them the more.

The other day I heard somebody say, "My, isn't it too bad that dogs live such a short time?" That puzzled me, and I went off to think about it, because it seems to me that I have lived an extraordinarily long time already. There has been so much to do and see.

I come to Him, and He lets me put my paw up on His leg to show that I love Him anew, with that fresh and delighted awareness which overwhelms a dog in his affections. (Ah, could you but know how it feels to be a dog, and to feel affectionate!) Then His hand touches my head gently. Sometimes He even scratches a little, and a shudder of joy goes through me as I keep looking up at Him.

Every-
body
Loves
to
Gossip

*A*nd guess who *else* was there—?"

"Not—?"

"You guessed it. Gerda Tackwell. And you should have seen what she was wearing!"

"Well, I suppose we oughtn't to gossip. But—"

"Darling, everybody loves to gossip. I love to gossip, you love to gossip. And I remember my father always saying that men were worse gossips than *women*."

"Was she accompanied by her son Mally? Dear little *Malvern*?"

"No, this was adults only."

"If you can call her *adult*."

"Actually I don't know *what* to call her. Do you?"

"If I had to typify her in—well, even one paragraph of well-chosen words—I'm afraid I'd flunk the test."

"Did you hear about her early morning call on Evelyn Lettsigg?"

"Lord, no!"

"Let me tell you. I think it was last Thursday, around noon. You know it was still vacation then, so Gerda was accompanied by little Mally. You know, Fred says that the child, instead of being named Malvern, ought to be named Mal*practice*. Anyway, she'd borrowed Evelyn's electric waffle-iron, and she came to return it—some ten days late, according to Evelyn. She ran across to the kitchen door and said, 'Hoo-hoo!' There she was with the waffle-iron, and little Mally in tow. Evelyn was just pouring some coffee for herself, so she invited her guest, in hospitable fashion, to sit down and have a cup of coffee. Meanwhile Mally was on the prowl. You know that lovely glass what-not that Evelyn's got, there at the corner of the dining room? Pretty soon there came the most terrific crash. Evelyn said she thought a knife was going through her. She jumped up— And what did the second Mrs. Tackwell do? She merely craned her pretty neck, and called into the dining room, in her most mellifluous phony finishing-school accents: 'Sonny boy, don't *do* that.' "

"Oh, my *God*. But what had he smashed?"

"An aqua crystal fish. One of those real museum pieces that Carl had brought her from Copenhagen, the last time he went to see his mother."

"Why, that's *criminal!*"

"Actually Evelyn swears that that woman never even rose from her chair. She said that she herself went in, and there was Mally, looking a little appalled, and the fish in several pieces on the slate floor. She said that she was absolutely white with rage. She couldn't allow herself to speak. She said, 'I stalked to the broom closet and got a broom and a dustpan, because I knew there were probably some splinters. I gathered up the pieces and put them on a paper.' She said that she had some vague notion that the thing might be glued back together again. But of course that was impossible. Young Mrs. Tackwell made a kind of clucking noise and said, 'Oh dear. But of course you'll allow me to replace it for you?' Evelyn said, 'If you *can*.' And, on Saturday, the second Mrs. Tackwell appeared with one of the most hideous *crockery fishes* that Heaven ever let loose."

"Oh, my *God!* You know, darling, if someone smashes something in the *Tackwell* residence, that's quite different."

"Have you heard what she said to Kip Bondley?"

"No, but let me tell this first. She had some people in for bridge, and Leah Vasswalter came along. Leah said she didn't want to accept the invitation but— You know: living right across the street— And of course Tacky himself has always been a great friend of Jack Vasswalter— Anyway, you know how *heavy* Leah is—"

"I'll say!"

"So Gerda Tackwell greeted her guest with her usual effusiveness. 'Oh, my dear, how nice of you to come. Sorry you were late. Now sit right down, because everybody's *dying* to hear about your trip to Hawaii. We're simply loaded with envy. Sit down right *here*.' And the chair she offered was a very fragile comb-back Windsor."

"Why, I remember the *very chair!* Maureen Tackwell bought it in Baltimore, just a couple of years before she was taken ill. You remember—she went there with Tacky to some kind of Johns Hopkins reunion or something? And she found several early American antiques."

"Yes, that was the one. Leah said she did have a few misgivings. She said, 'I thought, Little Old Me on *that* chair?' So she seated herself rather gingerly, and waited for the charming hostess to bring her cocktail. Gerda had gone over to the bar, and Leah said she leaned back in that chair, and then tried to correct her position— But it was too late. The whole back broke right off the chair when she leaned against it. Of course she shouldn't have been sitting there in the first place but—"

"Well, no one has any business having such a fragile chair in their living room, anyway."

"So, like I say, poor Leah leaned back, and there it was— Just like your story about the crystal fish and little Mally. *Crash*. That was it."

"Good thing Leah didn't fall over on the floor. She might have gone *through*."

"She said she felt like she wanted to. And the jolly hostess turned around and opened that wide mouth of hers and fairly screamed, 'Look at what you *did!*' Believe it or not, that was what she said."

"It's simply unbelievable that anyone in this world could be so gauche!"

"Ah, poor Tacky!"

"He asked for it when he married her. No one ever thought he *would*. You remember, they went around together for quit a while beforehand, when she first came to visit her sister—"

"I know, I know. But— Poor Tacky. Really, he looks dreadful. So worn and sad, all the time."

"What do you suppose it was? Purely a physical attraction?"

"It certainly wasn't a *mental* one."

"I should say *not*."

"Well, there was absolutely *nothing* to recommend her."

"Oh, I suppose she's good in bed. Or at least Tacky thought so, to begin with."

"Poor man, poor man!"

"I would say, offhand, that Tacky is easily the most popular doctor in town."

"That goes without saying. Everybody loves him to death."

"They say that women are prone to fall in love with their gynecologists. But actually I don't see how a gynecologist can ever fall in love, anyway."

"When one considers what he has to *see* and *do* in the course of a working day—"

"Darling, *please!*"

"Let's see: when were they married?"

"It's all of two years—"

"I remember exactly. It'll be three years next September. Mally wasn't more than three when we first saw him."

"Kip Bondley says that Gerda is his candidate for the most unpopular woman in Hamilton County."

"Tell him not to be so cruel. Just say that she's the most *eccentric*."

" *Eccen*tric? My God!"

"...A Kind of Animal Manna"

Dirty as a pig.
That's what people are always saying.
But not all pigs are dirty.

If you provide only dirt for a pig, he has to live in dirt. You would live in dirt, or I would live in dirt, if that were the only place we had to dwell. But give a pig plenty of greenery, and he is happy in it, and enjoys rooting roots, and grunting grunts, and living a respectable hog's life generally.

The word *pig* was used in manner of opprobrium long before dissident elements started calling policemen *pigs* and calling soldiers *pigs*. It's wicked for them to do so, but similar insults have been presented for a long time. A Frenchman hisses *cochon* at the person he despises; an Italian cries *porco;* your Spaniard speaks witheringly of *un cerdo;* and it's *Schwein,* naturally enough, in German.

It's enough to make a pig bristle his bristles.

At least Charles Lamb and his immortal Bo-bo knew a good thing when they saw and tasted it.

Yes, indeed.

Oink.

Weep No More, My Lady

*W*ater pipes are frozen in one area of this our County. Side roads lie drifted, even main roads are blocked in places. The snow is implacable. After it ceases descending, it keeps on blowing.

. . . Azaleas glow in the sub-tropical portion of this our County. Dooryards are a spasm of soft colors, and mockingbirds recognize and tell of it throughout their love-making.

Long ago the first pine woods were cropped away. Today big companies have gobbled up much of the land, but they offer a stewardship which individual owners seldom exemplified in the past. Fresh pines grow in the orderly rows of a vegetable garden.

Where native forests still rule there is springtime shade and song; but, in preparation, cotton and tobacco field stretch depressingly at this season.

> *Many days you have lingered*
> *Around my cabin door. . . .*
> *Oh, Hard Times, come again no more!*

White Springs, Jasper, Jennings: tiny towns still there. So are their store buildings, but so many with windows cracked or solid with dust . . . hamlets dying on or off the vine.

Here stands a stately frame house with galleries across the front. We can imagine an elderly lady living there, and imagine her living in that same house when she was young as well. We shall endow her with the name of Miss Francia . . . even when she was past eighty, and five times a great-grandmother, folks still spoke of her as Miss Francia. Let us say that she didn't like those newfangled cars and the smell and noise they made. Long ago she told her husband firmly, "Very well. You can get one of those gasoline buggies if you insist. But let me tell you this: I'll not ride in it. When I go out to drive, I'll go behind Old Pearl, way I always have." Thus she went, in her fine single buggy with red wheels, passing with dignity under streamers of tender moss, acknowledging the courtesy of acquaintances with a proud gesture.

She did not know that the day would come when there would be a gasoline pump smack in front of her door. Miss Francia wouldn't have approved.

But she is gone, gone, gone. . . . So is poor Willie Lee Pierce; and he was born when Miss Francia was quite elderly, back in 1934. But he too is removed, and the gravestone squats amid decaying tributes in a little corner of the landscape where black people lie.

> *Way down upon the Swanee River,*
> *Far, far away . . .*
> *There's where the old folks stay.*

The sightseeing boat is modeled somewhat after the manner of a stern-wheeler although it's powered by electricity. Tourists march aboard at stated hours, with bells of a carillon at the Stephen Foster Memorial clanging in their ears. Up and down the brown tannin-flavored silk of the Suwanee this craft goes plying. Bells in distance are still responding to guidance of the *carilloneur's* touch. Perhaps it is a tired performer who directs those chimes . . . or perhaps they are operated by tapes and the tape is worn a bit. If you are a rapt student of Fosteriana you can tell whether the tune is *The Camptown Races* or *Nellie Was a Lady* or *Gentle Annie*. If you are not a serious student of Fosteriana, the chances are that you can't tell one tune from another.

> *Now de orange trees am blooming*
> *On de sandy shore. . . .*

Passengers listen or do not listen to the guide as they journey smoothly. They look out to see fish jumping . . . once in a while a gator shows his nose, and everyone rises, exclaiming and pointing.

. . . Guide says, "A lot of people might not call Stephen Foster a genius, but by golly I say he was a genius. He *had* to be a genius, cause he wrote all those songs. Now, a lot of people say Stephen Foster was a drunk. Now, listen: he might have been an alcoholic, but he wasn't any drunk. He couldn't have been, cause he wrote all those songs. And I say to you, how could a *drunk* write all those songs? He might have been an *alcoholic*, but he wasn't any drunk. Take that from me!"

So we take it from him. And when the boat has landed, we take our departure as well, and go away past a decaying spa on the river's opposite bank. A cracked and empty swimming pool occupies a portion of landscape beside the spa— Oh, yes, Indians used to drink those waters—it was good for them. And white people came later to profit from their health-giving virtues, or so they thought. But those people died off, whether they drank the waters or whether they didn't drink them.

It is pleasanter to consider a lively swimming pool at our motel, where children are floundering and gay.

. . . Up the long straight road past unregimented forests (draglines and bulldozers mutter in the distance). So little original wildness left . . . cumulus drifts above tallest trees.

We glide into modernity, still preoccupied with the notion of an embittered young composer who fell to his doom across a washstand in a cheap New York hotel . . . and who, as he lay bleeding, might have entertained persistent dreams of a Suwanee River which he never saw and on whose banks he never set his feet.

In the New York confines of Hamilton County, the weather is still icy, as it was on that January night when Stephen Collins Foster died.

Unseen
Things
Above

*G*lory *in the highest, I will shout and sing. . . .*

When the roll is called, up Yonder, I'll be there. . . .

I'm here on business for my King.

As we savor the grand old hymns, we understand why the people who built our land had such courage and serenity in their faces.

They peer from archives of the Past. We find them gazing, alert and comprehending, in family albums or boxes of paling snapshots.

They dwell secure in the individual memory of any of us who clung to wrinkled hands of pioneers when first we tried to walk.

Oh, what a proud devotion! Our forefathers held an exulting belief in the resources of Eternity, and it gleamed and echoed in their choruses.

Let us be summoned to a renewed sacrament in the celebrated verities.

*H*ark! *'tis the Shepherd's voice I hear. . . .*

Work when the day grows brighter. . . .

Come and reign over us, Ancient of days!

Promise, hope, belief, fulfillment: there was nothing negative. It was all as exuberant as a bugle call.

Many persons scoff at the allegory represented in simple Faith, and regard it as clownish, rustic, outmoded. It is their privilege, like Levites, to pass by on the other side.

The rest of us are glad that hymns are still being sung.

We recognize the seamy side of organized religion. We have known dullards and charlatans as well as saints to occupy the pulpits.

We may choose to join in regular services, or we may choose not to.
But was anyone ever hurt by a hymn?
There are churches, large and small, all over Hamilton County.
And people singing in them.

I love to tell the story of unseen things above. . . .

There is gladness in my soul today. . . .

As on Thy highest mount I stand.

These phrases are not mere antique verbiage. Each listener, whether his first religious impression was gained from the more orderly accents of an older established church, or amid the chancels of some European temple— Or indeed, whether he was never truly exposed in childhood to any formal establishment of worship— Each listener can find a personal message amid such songs.

Long may our churches resound with the whole-souled utterance of folks whose belief in their Nation and in themselves is as boundless as their faith in the Lord.

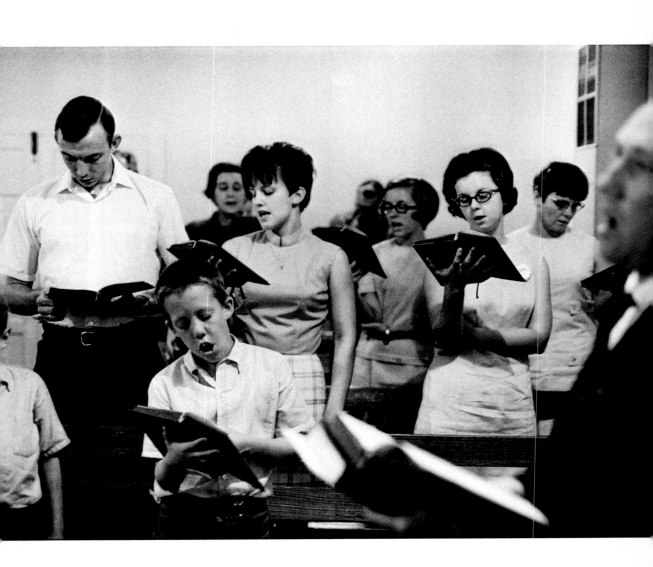

The Reverend Mr.

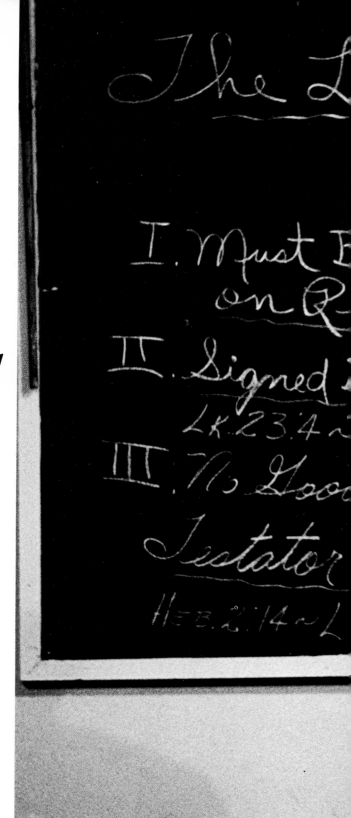

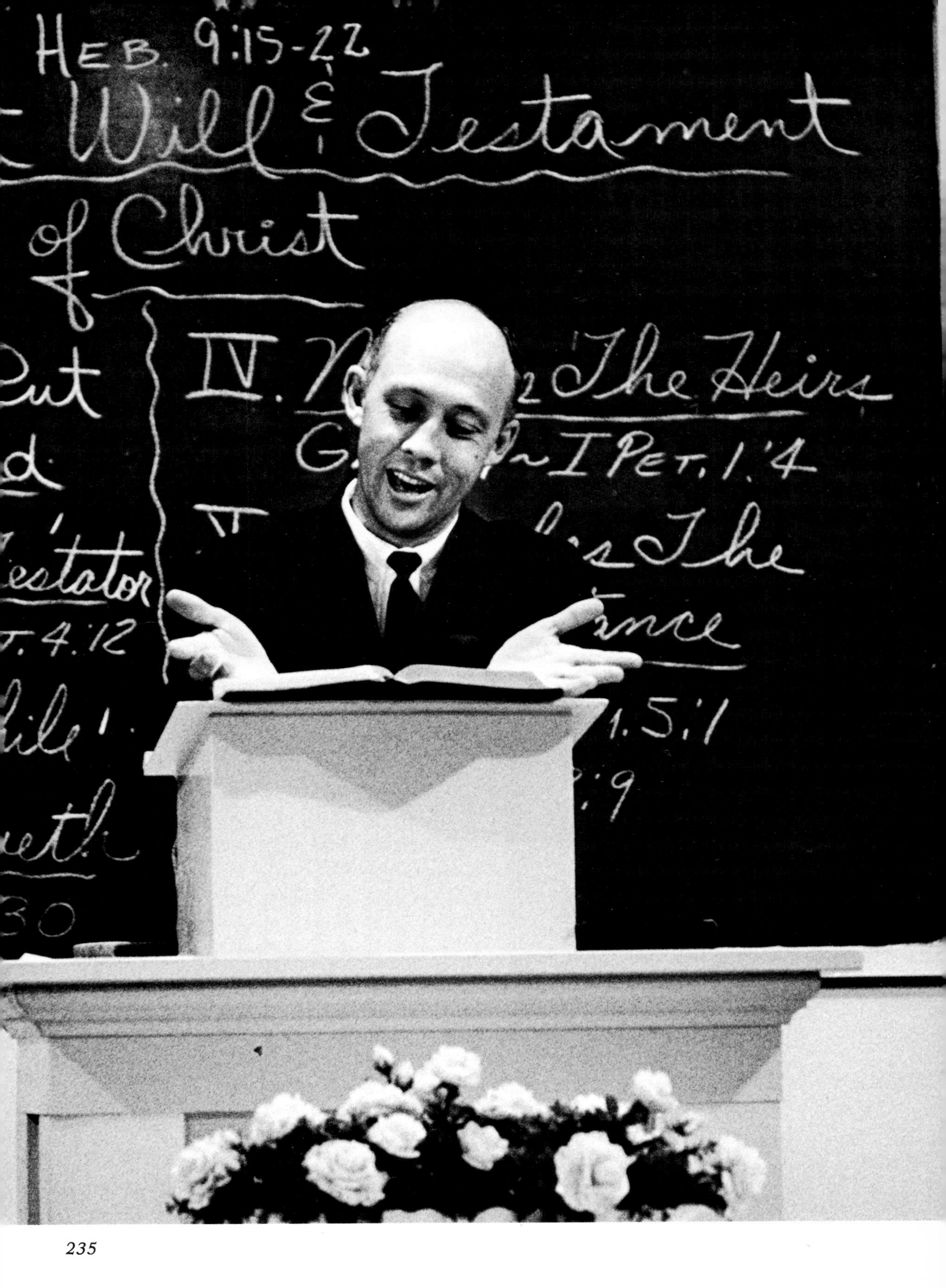
HEB. 9:15-22
Will & Testament
of Christ
The Heirs
I PET. 1:4

*T*he Reverend Mr. E. Powell Wardman of the Congregational Church was slightly below average height. He had a round head, small ears, and a shiny scalp of sea-shell pink. To cover the glare from people's eyes (a local jester once said) he wore throughout warm weather a narrow-brimmed white felt hat with a black band. During bitterest weather of winter he was apt to don an imitation lamb's-wool turban.

On this July day he journeyed with his poodle into a neighborhood known as Stumptown, a triangle between two sets of railroad tracks, where one of the few destitute members of his congregation was lying ill. He found the woman's health improved since the week before, and had the pleasure of presenting to her a small check sent by Mrs. Alice Aintree, a local banker's wife; also a plastic jar of stewed chicken sent by his own wife. He had attained to wisdom which deemed it unnecessary to pray or to read to any invalid a chapter from the Scriptures. Instead he allowed the woman to complain lengthily about her daughter and son-in-law, and he concluded the visit by reciting an amusing anecdote about Governor Bradford of seventeenth-century Plymouth. Then he untied Pris (the poodle was named Priscilla Mullins) from the porch post, and set out for home in amiable condition. He was prepared to greet with philosophic interest any small adventure which came his way; and now one emerged out of the earth itself.

Workmen from the telephone company were putting down a new cable, and they had found some queer substance in the excavation. Watchers crowded close, and palavered over splintered talcum-colored fragments which were passed from hand to hand. Not wood: bones, they all agreed . . . some mysterious sort of bones. When Wardman moved closer and requested that he might examine the relics, he knew at once what they were.

He told the men, and children who had gathered, that these were prehistoric remains—ivory, in fact—and that they were part of the tusk of a mammal known as the mastodon, of which there were several species, principally the genus *Mammut;* or of a mammoth, *Elephas Columbi,* an extinct elephant of post-Tertiary or Pleistocene times.

Reverend Wardman's face grew pinker and pinker, swollen with the satisfaction of his own knowledge. He went on to say that bones of much rarer creatures might lie buried far beneath the Hamilton County soil. He mentioned especially the *Allosaurus,* which had always interested him because of its ferocity; and the *Diplodocus* (although he could not quite remember which creature was the *Diplodocus*).

At any rate he spoke enthusiastically for five minutes and would have talked much longer, rolling out scientific names in the pedantic manner which he had worked hard to learn and from which he could no longer free himself, even when he wished to. But soon he found that he was lecturing only to little folks; the workmen, on learning that the discovery had no especial value in dollars and cents, had gone back to their digging. The foreman declared that he should turn the fragments over to the local construction manager. He carried away the largest pieces . . . boys had preëmpted a few chips.

The Reverend Mr. E. Powell Wardman walked through the business district, and thence up an avenue to his parsonage, with Pris rubbing her nose against clipped green grass of the lawns ahead. In imagination the minister enjoyed recreating a damp foggy steppe which had spread itself around a hill where the courthouse now stood, and which had been Hamilton County in truth long before this town was heard of, with its five thousand seven hundred and eighty-two souls.

In his mind he went out to slay a woolly rhinoceros, and to snare for food the broad-winged birds nesting on the tundras. He saw glaciers melted down, felt the swamp growing humid . . . in one pedestrian block he delved through millions of years, to witness black ferns growing a hundred feet high, and lame-brained lizards wallowing through them.

In this extensive past he found release and satisfaction, as surely as he had found them when he wrote his five-hundred-page-privately-printed historical novel, *Robin: A Romance of a Forgotten Abbey*, and as surely as he had not found release and satisfaction when he wrote his seventy-eight page query, *Why Is Man Here?*

He would have liked to sermonize about those scraps of brittle bone, the next Sunday. But he felt that, where his congregation was concerned, he might be treading upon dangerous ground. Pilgrims were a great deal safer, although not so conducive to blissful reverie. That was why he preached about the courageous Pilgrims frequently. They had landed in an unfamiliar world beset by savages and starvation, and no one in Hamilton County would ever have to do that.

Noble
Names

*B*ecause he had a passion for dates and figures and certainties, Evan Wulley regarded his task as a privilege which fell to few men.

When he worked in the Hamilton County courthouse during those years preceding his nominal retirement from active life, he was forever calling to account any younger clerks who did not exhibit his respect for commas or zeros.

"Didn't you ever make a mistake?" an annoyed and guilty youth flung at him one day. And after due thought Evan Wulley replied, "Yes. Yes, I did. Once." He was thinking of his wife when he said that; but the clerks could not know it, and would have been little interested had they known.

In spite of this self-incriminating admission, Evan came to be known as The Man Who Never Made a Mistake.

He retired in 1960. Nowadays, in spite of his calling himself a retired man, he presided through many hours each week as auditor at the Merchants' Bank. He divided his energies between this work, which helped to eke out his Social Security, and a more noble, delicate, and gratifying labor which he pursued ardently.

He was compiling a complete military record of every soldier who had enlisted in the Civil War from Hamilton County, or who had afterward established residence therein. He included also a handful of other an-cients—veterans of earlier wars or of the Indian campaigns, or of the Spanish–American fracas—who lay buried here and there. Occasionally Mr. Wulley was dazzled as he surveyed the men who'd served in his own First World War, the assembling of whose records would afford a statistical orgy unparalleled. And as for World War II— And then Korea— And now, Viet Nam—

He estimated that this undertaking would occupy him at least until he reached the age of one hundred years. Accordingly he still had twenty-nine years to go.

Drawers of an oak desk in the Wulley living-room were filled with masses of manuscript inscribed in Evan's square-lettered hand. The resonance of names gave him solace in haunted hours of the night when often he was compelled to wrestle with his wife as furiously as any saint ever wrestled with the Devil.

Then, the battle won, he would crawl back into bed. Breathing the thick air of his slant-ceiled room, he would invoke the roster of those whose living and dying had claimed his love. For one of his age could remember when many of them were alive and walking.

Apolos W. Maffitt, Stephen Curroo, Isaac Morrow, Bartlett Stone, Thomas McMint, Anton Lain, Lyman Clark, Caleb Hartshorn, Delmar Lake: those were people who counted, and many more like them. The chant of their names—so predominantly Gaelic or Norman or Anglo-Saxon, and so encouraging—carried the earnest quality of an elder hymn.

Had he possessed gifts of drama and imagery, he would have bugled the men up, for him to look again at their faces and to take strength from the knowledge that they, now sainted by the process of death, had been men with problems perhaps much worse than his own . . . men who, in some cases, solved those problems with a courage and sanity which was generally attributed (not with ample justice) to their entire generation.

But they were only names and dates. As the years piled around him, Evan Wulley felt a mild surprise when he recognized that it did not take long for a person whom he had known well—with whom he had eaten and drunk and pursued the ordinary intercourse of business or religion— It did not take long for such to become only proper names cut into stone, and followed by a series of Septembers and Junes and Mays, of tenths and twenty-seconds and thirty-firsts.

. . . This night, on hearing his wife creeping to the stairway, Evan got out of bed promptly. Tense and shivering, he went down and intercepted Thelma, who wore an old sweater around her night-gowned shoulders, just as she was charging onto the porch.

"They're here! I heard em—"

"Now, now. Thelma. They won't bother anything."

She moaned, "I heard em come," and she was waving a flashlight around . . . just a flashlight. Sometimes she had a kitchen knife or a pair of scissors with which she contemplated attack on the thieves, and it was difficult to wrest such weapons away from her. He had been painfully cut three or four times, in the process.

Evan counseled, "I don't think you ought to be out in all this damp. They'll go away—just see if they don't—"

She protested still, and shuddered with fear of the loss which might come to her, but at last he got the door closed, and persuaded her to come to the little front window. There she could squeeze her face against the pane, and peer out into the dim tangle of bushes.

"See, Thelma? There isn't anybody there. I wouldn't let them get your roses, anyway!"

"They dig em up," she mourned, "every time they get a chance!" But tonight she wasn't seriously violent, and at last he took the flashlight from her and saw her safely to bed.

Back in his own chamber once more, his thoughts went from his son in Oregon to the few friends who'd told him repeatedly that he ought to do something about Thelma (put her in a public institution, they meant); and from them he wandered through ledgers and regimental histories, back into his own room once more, and to the black corner behind his dresser where a piece of insignia on its metal staff stood waiting his need of it—all complete, all arranged, even to the rolled-up, unfaded cotton flag which would be set in the slot.

Evan Wulley went drifting into slumber, accompanied to the uttermost boundaries of consciousness by a list of firm and gratifying names. Joseph Pressley, Charles Wickware, Humphrey Hillock, William Ennis, George W. Flowers, Jesse Burgess, John Dutcher, Samuel Gilpin, Asa Wren, Kendall Young: these and others of unfaltering cadence marshaled themselves in orderly fashion and permitted him to sleep, gratified to recognize that there could be little error—and no madness whatsoever —in any of them.

His
Holy
Arm

. . . For he hath done marvellous things: his right hand, and his holy arm, hath gotten him the victory.

PSALMS: 98:1

Charley Lannox had been documented before the world as a hero. Such canonization was only six hours in the past; but he recognized himself as a coward when he lay in clean quiet darkness of his own house and heard sounds in the unfinished attic overhead.

Charley didn't know how long he had been lying awake before he recognized the intruder's menace for what it was. At first he thought he was imagining things. Maybe it was the beer—maybe he had been thinking too intently about the past when he went to sleep before midnight. Possibly it was the tension, the unusual excitement of that evening and its ceremony which left his shrunken body quivering and made raw substance of his nerves.

There sounded a scurry followed by noticeable stealth . . . prowling among beams . . . the certainty of an enemy lurking a few feet distant, restrained solely by the physical restriction of sloping wallboards which Lannox himself had nailed into place.

As the man waited stiff and trembling, staring up at paleness of the ceiling, he owned swift visions of the other valiant Charley.

One entity he embraced as his own in daytimes when he rode abroad with efficiency, and was draped in the mantle of Government service. Charley had worked in the Post Office Department for more than half a century.

As a boy he'd helped his grandfather and father at the fishing-camp-boat-rental place they owned, up the river near Harrison. He didn't earn much—just the couple of dollars which his father offered now and then, when Charley wanted to go to the movies or to a tent show . . . sometimes Grandpa Parton would add a fifty-cent piece to that.

When the postmaster came to hire a boat and try to catch himself some catfish, he measured young Charley and noticed also that the youth owned a bicycle in good condition. Charley was engaged as a special-delivery messenger, part time. He proved loyal and dependable. Later he helped out in the office itself during the Christmas rush. Doubtless he would have graduated through normal dignity of Civil Service to full-time occupation without any interlude, if the war hadn't come along.

At seventeen Charley Lannox turned into a hard-working, uncomplaining soldier who kept out of trouble ordinarily, who was never too sharp to look at, and yet exhibited a pride in his occupation. He was round-shouldered even in the days before he lugged constantly a weighty bag of mail. He was thin-chested, long-nosed—the string-bean type who might never appear as a beau-ideal buck private, no matter how hard he tried. His puttees were never quite right. He could not wrap them so that they tapered smartly; always they were too full at the ankle or above the calf. Yet his sober uniform was neat and well brushed . . . it never seemed to fit him.

Charley had a pointed chin and flap-shaped ears. His hair line receded early, and there was a bald place at the part before he was well out of uniform. He'd been through the St. Mihiel show in middle September, and went all the way through the Argonne without getting hit. As one of the beaten ugly vertebrae in the Army's backbone he held up well.

. . . There was something about a citation. His friends didn't recall many details until the matter was investigated years later. There weren't many decorations floating around, ready to be handed to doughboys in the First World War—no Good Conduct Medals, no Purple Hearts, no Bronze or Silver Stars. Every once in a while a few French Croix de Guerre were doled out, and people kidded about winning them in crap games.

Rarely somebody was decorated with the D.S.C. . . . otherwise it was just a written citation, if the officers decided that you deserved one.

Later there circulated gossip about little silver stars to be worn on the Victory ribbons: a bronze star for each major engagement, a silver one for each citation. Most folks never saw any of the silver stars. The Silver Star medal, as such, was instituted a long time afterward, when Charley Lannox was just a mailman slouching up and down business stairways, before he graduated to the comfort of wheels.

. . . Charley had his Silver Star at last, and he was a hero, and he lay alone in his suburban house. His son was a major in the Air Force in Hawaii, his daughter long since married and living in Nashville.

(His wife dwelt apart in a sunglared flatland where it seemed that the growl of superhighway traffic might well disturb even the tired dead.)

Charley was nearly seventy years old. But he still loved the route over which he'd driven in one Government vehicle after another, ever since his children were away down in the baby grades. The thought of mandatory retirement, so soon to be inflicted upon him, was an ache.

. . . Paws running, threatening in the attic . . . he knew just what sort of paws they were. Sweat on his plaster forehead was a pearling ooze which betokened a chill to come—a wet rash, as might have arisen from fever. There was nothing for Charley Lannox to do, it seemed, but crouch and suffer.

He thought wildly, "If only somebody was here in the house *with* me!"

. . . You could manage aggravating tasks a lot better because of the mere fact that people depended on you. Kids, for instance. If Les or Sally still lived at home, as in those days before Myrtle had her operation and died of it— If the children were around, he would naturally have to be bold and gay.

But there was no one. His house sat near the edge of a more recently constructed subdivision. Charley had purchased the property toilsomely, long before the city began to expand in an easterly direction. Nowadays there sprouted many ranch-type houses pristinely white or tinted green or pink in sunshine, broad with picture-window lights in the dark. Neighbors, yes; but none of them close.

Even a next-door neighbor wouldn't have done any good on this night. Charley recognized that he was beset by a familiar terror. Frequently he'd said weakly, "Guess I'll have to do something about this," but he had never done it.

Oh, he'd gone out into the neat storage closet between back door and garage. He'd examined the narrow trap-door with its rectangle of copper screening. He speculated, "Well, it didn't get in that way, not into the attic." Charley walked outside and examined both ends of the roof's peaking, sheltered by eaves. All appeared tight.

"Must have come up through the walls." He beat a retreat, and blessed his stars during any long evening when he heard no movement in the attic.

There had been an invasion or two after that . . . none recently. In this solitary black hour, amid the threatening witchery of three a.m., he perceived that the agony he now endured was a compounding of other historic frights he'd more or less ignored.

Men talked about something like that, down at the Legion hall one night. Some of the members lingered at the bar. They had been playing cards . . . the game broke up always at eleven . . . folks were drinking their go-home-and-go-to-bed drinks, when old Luke Pray began to laugh.

That was not too long after Luke first moved down to the Chattanooga area. It was a delicious novelty for Charley Lannox to encounter him. He had not seen Luke since 1919, not until that day when Luke, fat and bald and seamy-faced, halted Charley in front of the bank.

"Hey. Your face looks familiar to me. . . ."

Charley's old top sergeant, and Doc Wilsey's top sergeant too! Luke was vacationing along with his wife . . . official retirement from a railroad job was due to occur in the near future, and he and Mrs. Pray were looking around for a place to spend their permanent second honeymoon. Perhaps it was not the mere presence of both Charley and Doc Wilsey which finally tipped the balance in favor of Hamilton County. But anyway they were glad to have Luke living near.

. . . Luke started laughing into his big paper cup of beer. "I was just thinking of one time I saw Charley jump."

"When was that?'"

"I think it was before St. Mihiel. Some little town— I forget the name. Captain Denham wanted some loose lumber to fix up his billet, and we heard there was some, in an old shed behind a church. You remember how hard it was to find a board or anything like that, in France? Those frogs used to build everything out of stone."

He said, "I took Charley and some other fellow along with me, and we went hunting for that shed. It was pitch-dark and rainy, and there were two or three sheds, all of them built of stone, all more or less shot up. We didn't know which was the one with the boards in it."

Luke swallowed the last of his drink. "I said, 'Lannox, you go inside and strike a match, and see whether you can find anything.' There was a lot of peeping—you know, like chickens make—and I figured we would have to clean those boards real good if chickens had been roosting all over them."

Doc Wilsey knew what was coming, he remembered the incident. Charley had told him one time, speaking in that gush of trivial confidence with which men necessarily indulge themselves in battle areas.

Doc looked over at Charley. Lannox was leaning at the end of the bar, knobby-shouldered, thin-faced . . . homely, neat. He wore a sports jacket which Les, his son, had deeded to his father. The jacket didn't fit Charley at all.

Luke Pray related: "So I had a flashlight, and I went on to the next shed, and I sent the other soldier to the one beyond that. Hadn't any more flashed the light when I heard an awful yell from Charley. We came running back, and I shot my light inside, and there he was."

He shook with laughter. "Rats! The lumber was there all right, but those weren't chickens that had been running around: they were rats, and mighty big ones too. Charley was clear up on the pile of boards—he must have landed there in one jump. I bet he broke the world's record for standing high jump and never even knew it. All around him those rats were jumping and chasing back and forth, squeaking every which way. He was hollering—"

Luke made a falsetto of his voice. " 'Sergeant! Save me! *Help!* Sergeant!' "

It was amusing enough for old veterans to stand and contemplate a boy who was frightened by rats in France, fifty years before. Through the agitation of laughter even Charley managed to giggle, but his heart didn't seem to be in it.

Luke and Doc Wilsey walked home together. Doc said, "Luke, that wasn't any joke. Not for Charley."

Luke Pray peered at his friend through the moonlight. "What do you mean?" He chuckled again. "Poor little old Charley! But—pshaw—he didn't mind my telling a yarn on him."

"That isn't what I mean. I mean the rats."

"Why, they wouldn't have bit him. They got out of there fast. Ran and hid in their holes, soon as I flashed my light."

The doctor found it difficult to make his meaning clear. . . . It wasn't what the rats actually could have done to Charley Lannon. It was he—Charley—his fear of rats.

Luke seemed puzzled.

"Take your wife,'" said Wilsey. "When you folks were over, playing canasta with Bessie and me the other night, our little Siamese cat walked into the room. Remember how Ada acted?"

Luke Pray said, "That's a funny thing about Ada. She's scared to death of cats. Been that way, ever since she can remember."

"Some people are that way about snakes, Luke. Some about dogs, or bugs, or even horses. With Charley, it's rats and mice."

They had halted in front of the doctor's house. "Funny thing," Luke kept saying. "You mean Charley was actually frightened to death?"

"He was scared green."

Luke Pray remained silent for a moment or two. Then he said slowly, "One time we were getting a lot of shelling. It was somewhere up in the Argonne, and those were our own shells. We had to get word back to the artillery to change their range. I called for volunteers. Seems like Charley responded."

Doc Wilsey nodded. "Wasn't there a citation or something? Maybe in a despatch or somewhere? Seems like—"

"Seems like there was," said Luke. "I'll try to find out."

Even in 1970 there are still the ancient Purple Hearts being shipped around. Once a man was punctured by a rifle bullet or a hot scrap of metal from a Five-Point-Nine . . . wound burned, fever came, gauze slabs were bound into place and soaked and thrown away. Eventually came healing . . . but lists and data can be fouled, even when records are only a few days old.

Some of those belated enameled wafers are shunted through the mails today, when blood which spotted at Soissons has long since been vanished by sun and wind, when the soil has been scraped away, when twists of scar tissue are so silver that they seem like birthmarks.

Charles Parton Lannox stood, hollow-chested and twitching, while a beribboned brigadier-general, who had traveled many miles for the purpose, declared that the citation should be read aloud. The general fastened the Silver Star, dangling on its striped silk, to the fabric of Charley's somewhat rumpled Sunday suit.

. . . For gallantry in action near Bon Vache, France, on 16 October, 1918. Private Lannox, whose platoon had been cut off by artillery fire of supporting batteries and was suffering severe casualties, volunteered to carry a message to the artillery commander.

With courage and initiative he covered the distance in the face of severe attack by the enemy, this act calling for bravery above and beyond the call of duty. Through Private Lannox's efforts, the range of artillery fire was altered and the survivors of his platoon were enabled to withdraw.

It had taken months, and a lot of correspondence. The colonel of Charley's regiment was long since dead, but Captain Denham was discovered to be still living in Pasadena; and Denham accomplished wonders in securing the necessary affidavits. The Awards and Decorations branch of the Adjutant General's Office did the rest.

A newspaper photographer was present, and a picture would appear in the *News–Free Press*, the *Times*, or the *Post*—Charley didn't know which. The photo would reveal that many of the Legionnaires looked as old as Spanish War veterans, and that Charley Lannox had his eyes tightly shut.

Drinks flowed afterward, hands were laid in approval on Charley's shoulder. It was unfortunate that his son was thousands of miles away— that his daughter had just undergone a hysterectomy and didn't dare make the trip from Nashville to witness this ceremony . . . men drank three or four beers instead of their usual one or two. Homer Hebb made a speech, and Roger Flory started to sing "Mademoiselle from Armentieres" but most of those present had forgotten the words.

Charley went home and slept. Then he was awakened by the rat.

His panic stemmed not alone from the fact that a creature he feared and loathed was creeping in proximity. Also he shuddered under the awful knowledge that this torture had been endured before, that it would come again, that he might never open the door on his forsaken quarters (especially at night!) without recognizing the possibility of a hairy Presence.

His house was as right and tight and well-behaved as his own professional existence. Also it was nearly as pathetic with forlornness as Charley Lannox himself. The house held its package of intimate memories . . . Myrtle had lain there, not able to take joy in fresh-painted walls or the clean new floor beneath her slippers when she labored to and from the bathroom. She'd gone from this house to the hospital. She'd never come back in life or death; but her personality, her hard-working dignity and former serenity, were in the low-ceiled rooms. So was the reflection of her children.

In that tiny squeezed vestibule Charley had brandished the law to his son when Lester went dissipating at a roadside joint after a high-school dance. . . . Charley had turned on that wan porch light to welcome his daughter's first escorts. He had talked to her in halting embarrassment about personal things—things you had to talk to a girl about, if her mother was dead, if her aunt was a screeching religious fanatic who found no importance in the flesh.

Home. . . . How many hundred hours had Charley worked, from the first rise of bare yellow scaffolding—mixing mortar, lugging concrete blocks, putting on siding, doing the things he needed to do and learned to do, else he might not have his house to dwell in?

The rat was taking over. This was the third or fourth time he had heard the rat—the hundredth time he had cringed from the thought and sought to ignore it.

First he called himself a hero, and tried to remember how brave he had been in that antique war. Only hours ago the Government had given him a medal. Gallantry in action? Possibly so, possibly so. People who contrived the citation must believe that they were speaking truth. As a matter of fact, Charley Lannox had not been conscious of being gallant at all.

He recollected a chill of ordinary human trepidation and annoyance because he had to journey over slopes of wet clay. He wished that the shelling would stop, that he would never have to listen to exploding shells again, or to the nervous engine-backfiring sound of water-cooled machine guns handled by the enemy.

In fact he had seen only three enemies on that fateful day. They looked like wet tramps with misshapen metal hoods on their heads . . . the scuttled helmets seemed too big for them . . . they ducked along a ridge into the Argonne brush. Then Charley Lannox arose and went seeking the Post of Command, because the sergeant had happened to look his way when he called for volunteers.

Cinders, the juicy road, mess gear stuck upon his heel. Yes, he remembered that mess tin. It had been flattened by one vehicle, perhaps pushed up to form a bent trap by other wheels. When Charley's muddy shoe struck against it, the object closed its metal jaws. He limped, kicking along the roadside ditch, trying to shake the thing loose.

In boyish musings he'd contemplated glory. He'd entertained an illusion of himself grown suddenly taller and more handsome—trim, tight-uniformed—his helmet glinting at a rakish angle. . . . He pounced from machine-gun nest to machine-gun nest, with a Colt automatic in each hand and plethoric ammunition and grenades to back them up.

He'd visualized an heroic Charley

thus. He had not considered dancing around in squashed clay, trying to kick a can loose from his heel.

That was the past, gone so long that he blinked at contemplating the vanished decades. Thousands of men —hundreds of thousands—had been slain in the service of America since then. Multitudes of youths they were, with officers' insignia and without . . . they were not even born—in many cases their parents were not even born—on that neglected Argonne afternoon.

The wrath of accumulated time was frightening, but never so terrifying as the rodent infesting the attic. It sounded like a desperate pony.

Charley thought, "It's going to be the rat's house or mine, pretty quick —one or the other." He attempted to shift his bare heel over the edge of the bed beneath the tightening sheet . . . couldn't move his leg. The leg was lead or maybe wood—dry as a scrawny branch of charred pine. Couldn't budge it.

He thought wildly of his life and his route and the people thereon. Mrs. Kitty Rummel owed him thirty-seven cents for postage due. Repeatedly he had put a note in her box, with other mail, but now she was gone to Florida. She would never remember to pay him.

No—good Lord, good Lord!—it was a *dollar* and thirty-seven cents!

All those little red stamps affixed to forwarded copies of her Christian Science magazines, and she had gone back to Coral Gables. She'd forgotten. He would never get his dollar-thirty-seven.

So he thought of his route, he thought of old mail boxes weathering on their posts . . . new ones, hard and glaring, stiff tin flags saluting to hail Charley down. Boxes, circulars, straps and rubber bands around them, endless sorting and ticketing at the post office in early mornings, little Registered slips to be signed . . . his horn honking, honking to summon people down driveways.

The rat walked above, it crouched fairly overhead. Lannox knew that its teeth were gnawing the wallboard, ready to make a hole therein; soon he would see the awful teeth themselves, the beady eyes and whiskers. His soul screamed anguish at mere suggestion of that tapered tail with its shining.

. . . Rat went far to the other end of the house, Lannox heard it galloping. Then back it came. It was all over the place, talking in high-pitched cheeping gibberish, saying, "Charley, I've come to live in your house. The house is mine, Charley. Mine!"

He thought of Mrs. Summerton,

halfway along his route, and it was years—oh, many many years before — Sally was a sophomore, and going to march at the game. The local football team had its feminine auxiliary, and Sally was to appear in a costume of school colors. . . . Lester served as substitute tackle . . . he might get a chance in the last quarter, if the locals were leading the visitors by at least two touchdowns.

And there he was, Charley With the Mail, driving from box to box along the road and wondering how the hell he was going to manage to buy a new blouse for his daughter, so's she could march at the game. They cost two-sixty-five apiece, those blouses, if you bought them ready made. He had to buy one ready made. His wife wasn't alive to sew it . . . the girl had tried. She'd broken down in tears, and ruined the material.

Permeated with this worry, and still giving proper attention to mail at the same time, the electric horror of Mrs. Summerton's screech ripped his ears.

She occupied the front step of her house, wringing hands, and laughing and jigging up and down, and calling, "Ooooh! Mr. Lannox! Eeeee! I'm glad you came by. I'm here all alone, and the trap just went off, and you got to take it out for me. I just don't *dare* handle a dead *mouse*. Ooooh!"

. . . Opening the ten-ton car door,

his slow step on the grass and flagstones, the pleasantry he tried to murmur. Something about, "Now, now, don't take on so. It's just a mouse. Where is that old trap, anyway?"

She pointed, and there it was, down behind a chest in the dining room. Her Dachshund barked at the aperture behind the chest; and Charley had to get a yardstick and pull the Thing out, trap and all. There was blackness . . . he remembered mumbling something about a newspaper. She gave him an old newspaper and wrapped it carefully.

"My," she said, as he carried it to the garbage can, "I'm certainly glad a man came along."

A man, he thought. Jesus. A man!

Minutes later he had to park suddenly. He got out of the car, weaving, retching . . . fortunately no other cars drove past while he was being sick.

The most terrified citizen in Hamilton County hauled himself into attic space and stood confined, crouching beneath the weight of the roof, with the trap-door closed tightly behind him. He was Charley Lannox, he wore tennis shoes and no socks, he wore an old sweater and pajama trousers, and in his left hand he carried a cheap plastic flashlight.

His right hand held a weapon. It had been tempered and stamped in Massachusetts more than a century before. Its blade was long and curving. A Chicopee saber: Grandpa Parton, fighting under Joe Wheeler, took it from a captured Yankee during the wintry campaign up Knoxville way. When he was a child, Charley found joy in rubbing his fingers over the metal twistings of the hilt.

This saber he had rediscovered in the closet of Lester's bedroom, after rejecting whatever other implements suggested themselves. There were no firearms in that house. Charley's son had indeed owned a .410 shotgun, but that had been shipped to Lester when he was stationed in Texas. Anyway a shotgun would blow a hole in the ceiling if Charley fired it at the rat.

He crawled up in trembling sickness solely because there was no choice in the matter. He had been brought to bay by this vile happenstance. This was Korea, this was Viet Nam all over again. The age was an age of murder, threat, protracted alarm. The rat was in the house.

Either it's going to be your house, or it's going to be the rat's. Somebody has to get rid of the rat.

Somebody?

There is only you.

Charley Lannox needed to live in peace and comfort. He might not dwell that way, if something he feared and hated was malignant nearby.

Vaguely he sought to invoke martial words or hymns. He tried to inspirit himself, as Scottish soldiers were alleged to do . . . bagpipes of his soul were muted, so were the drums. A phrase came. *Don't fire 'til you see the whites of their eyes.* Everyone always quoted that, but Charley could not name the author amid the few shreds of tattered tradition which clung in his recollection. . . . *Quarante Hommes et Huit Cheveaux.* The old Forty-and-Eight stuff—the long ago war, the conflict wherein he had earned that medal in its black-and-gilt box upon his dresser. . . . *Lafayette, we are here.*

He heard the rat again. It was beyond him, dashing pell-mell. Charley sobbed . . . silly figure: pajamas, gray sweater, that hoary saber in his hand.

He balanced precariously from joist to joist. How far apart were the timbers? Sixteen inches, was it? A brief vision of the half-built house came amid pine and cedar smells and the scent of dust and, worse than that, the noxious if imagined odor of an antagonist nearby . . . sixteen inches? Thirty-three? Couldn't be that wide.

There were a few loose planks scattered. Charley saw with loathing that this beast or perhaps another preceding it had stained the dusty planks with dung. Those boards had been placed by plumbers or electricians: there were necessary black pipes venting up from the bathroom below, there were heavy electric cables in plain sight. Nothing else—no, nothing. How had that rat ever gotten there in the first place? Through the walls?

More in a nervous gesture than with deliberate intent, Charley's thin finger trembled against the flashlight switch. Suddenly he stood in stuffy darkness.

A light! It came from somewhere far outside . . . he waited . . . light touched his eyes again and vanished. He waited, again it reappeared. Then he knew, the whole thing was plain to him.

Shingles had been torn, near the edge of the roof which overshot the lower garage structure. This damage was not visible from the yard outside or from the driveway; doubtless the shingles were scalped off by a recent storm. It was only a little hole, a sidewise hole: thus no serious roof-leak had developed. But an airline beacon, twisting on its tower a few miles away, gave Charley the clue he needed.

This was an accomplishment, if not a victory or even an indication of success in frightful encounter. With something like hope in his heart, he switched on the flashlight again and balanced precariously across joists— moving slowly, daring no misstep whereby he would crush his weight through the thin composition which made the ceiling.

He lifted one of the planks. His saber clattered, he fancied that the lurking rat snarled a response. He put aside the old sword, and managed to wedge a short slab of pine against the low hole at the end of the gable. . . . There, it was done. The rat had won its way to the interior, but could not escape now—not from that prison where they both stood caged.

The next day Charley would manage a permanent repair job with shingles and nails and heavy screening . . . next day? No, that day precisely. It was three-thirty in the morning now. The Legion hall seemed a million years behind, so did the general's voice and the young aide's voice, rattling the citation.

Charley Lannox must be bold because the world had ticketed him so. He picked up the saber again and moved into battle.

. . . For pity's sake, how *long* was this house? It seemed very small indeed when viewed in common perspective: snug kitchen, a bath and a half, combination living and dining room, three bedrooms (two of them tiny). Not a large house . . . but in this hour the attic became a spectral cavern, stretching through infinity— it seemed that he could never reach the end.

Go he must. That was where he heard the rat moving. Over there, far at the other gable end.

. . . No, no—here, here—scarcely an arm's length away!

The animal rushed up over a joist and the beam went wild in Charley's uncertain hand, again a hard yellowness bit the creature. Eyes, hideous tail—he saw it—it was huge. A rabid rat, no doubt, and seeming to sputter through nasty jaws as it stared from its perch on the very two-by-four where he poised.

It sped away, it ran into lowest darkness of the eave-side. But his shaft hunted and found it again. Grunting with pain as his head scraped a rafter, Charley advanced.

. . . He was all Decent Humanity on a secluded mountain where danger pressed. Oh, if only he had a gun! Cheerfully he would have blasted a hole in the ceiling in the process of exploding this malicious foe—it would have been easier. An entire new ceiling for one of the rooms would have cost mere coppers in the coin of his strength.

Ah, a tiger charging—a hairy demon with writhing worm for a tail! The Thing dashed next to Charley's ankles, he teetered in frenzy, he rapped out with the saber point and felt it jab through a ceiling panel, heard nails protesting the blow.

Again the avenging flashlight, again beaded eyes to reflect a prick-

ling hate. The rat had rushed to the far end.

Why had he put up that board to block the hole? He could have herded the creature out of there, and then stuffed the hole; no one would be the wiser.

No one. Except himself.

Charley Lannox's picture in the Sunday paper . . . he would treasure the clippings and send copies to children and grandchildren. Accept congratulations from well-meaning people along his mail route. Hear fellows down at the Legion talking about, "You remember—the night they hung the medal on Charley?"

These delights to be experienced. But in secret conscience he would be compelled to face the barren knowledge that he was never brave as the world thought him to be.

Crouched in misery he crept, shabby tennis shoes pressing the timbers.

All my life . . . this ugly fear. Furry crawling things . . . the slick shine of their tails, dirt they leave behind, the taint they carry.

All evil, all menace bound in hair, hide and feet of rodents like these.

Oh, Lord . . . he's waiting for me now! I can see the foam he's spitting. Yes—rabid—like a dog—I know it, I know it! And ready to attack, and realizing how afraid I am.

And squeaking.

If only he'd not make that noise. If only—

The man bumped his head once more, sharpness was there to tear the skin apart. Blood ran down, Charley did not care. He was close, the Thing was in a corner, it gave a leap to one side. He lashed with the blade. Missed.

The rat bounded back again. Then the flashlight— Lower, lower, shrinking, weakening, it oozed from yellowness to orange, it had been white when first he climbed there.

The battery. When had he changed that battery in the flashlight?

A weakening and running out, an awful redness, only brown the glow . . . brown. Out.

In the final ooze of light which Heaven awarded him, Charley lunged.

The point of Grandpa Parton's captured blade sank home.

One small cry.

Silence.

He had a paper of matches in his sweater pocket, and so the final nightmare was expedited. Trap-door again . . . remove the cover . . . process of putting the hilt handy, close to the opening. Slow climb down, knees so weak and teetering, the business of drawing down the saber with its burden heavy and impaled. Visit to the garden. Shovel cutting and thudding in gloom.

Charley came back inside. He had sprayed a garden-hose across the sword and rinsed the traces off. He washed the Chicopee saber again and again. Smears were vanished . . . vaguely he considered boiling the blade, but that might take the temper out. And it was a weapon to be honored in the future as he had never honored it before.

There by the kitchen sink he scrubbed it hard with soap and water, and used a polish too; he thrilled as he saw bits of brightness which still survived amid rust. Back into its scabbard he ran the blade and leaned it in a corner.

He went to reverence the pictures of his wife and children. Myrtle smiled as she had smiled in those tender years before she faded. Here was Sally in her wedding dress, with Ben beside her; here was Les with wings upon his chest.

Here was Charley Lannox, going back to bed to lie alone and flat, Merthiolate stinging his skull—exhausted, worn, but replete with fresh great pride.

$\mathcal{C}$an you remember?

There wasn't much fruit juice sold in elder grocery stores. Just grape juice, perhaps.

(Henry Alkire used to keep a barrel of cider on tap at his store during autumn and winter months, and you'd buy it by the jugful.)

. . . Not too much in the way of fresh vegetables, either. Oh, there'd be occasional baskets of roasting ears, in season, and sometimes a few other varieties available for families who didn't have any gardens, or maybe those who lived up over stores on Main Street in stuffy so-called apartments, and weren't visited by the peddlers who drove about town. . . . Mr. Frank and Mr. Bourne and Mr. Kinman were truck gardeners, and vended green things from door to door.

There were vegetables in cans. . . .

(Freezing was something that happened to your fingers or your toes or your nose during a blizzard.)

Most grocery stores didn't sell meat, either. Meat you bought at the butcher shop. And, earlier than that, some of the farmers or ranchers who did their own butchering would drive around, and slice off a steak or a roast, and weigh it right there, in front of your house.

Oh sure, they sold *lard* at grocery stores. It came in tubs.

Bananas hung in a huge bunch in the front window—upside down, opposite from the way they grow naturally. Grocers were always telling about tarantulas and other dangerous forms of tropical life which would come scuttling out of the bananas when they were cutting off an order. A banana knife was curved and sharp, something like a scimitar, and was kept stuck into the stem when not in use. One time Uncle Jack Sheldon was cutting off some bananas from a bunch, and out came a furry tarantula. Uncle Jack impaled it with his banana knife, and everybody stood around and gaped at the monster. They put it on a paper in the window, for customers to see. Women shuddered, the little girls squealed and pointed.

*K*egs of pickles were kept in the basement where it was dim and cool . . . keg of sweet pickles, keg of dills. Clerks were continually loping up and down the basement stairs. For dried apricots and dried peaches, and almonds and raisins and walnut meats—those also were retained in the sweet-smelling cellar. They came from California in flat wooden boxes.

A barrel of starch stood handy upstairs, and old Germans who ambled into the store would often scoop up some starch, and munch it while they made their rounds. Coffee beans were shipped in bulging brown sacks; the tea was in bulk, too, in a series of red tin bins . . . fascinating bins, with pictures of coolies and other Asiatics painted on the sides, along with names of the different kinds of tea: Oolong, Pekoe, Gunpowder, Ceylon, English Breakfast. . . .

Crackers came in barrels or boxes, and cheese loomed golden in huge rounds covered by glass. Those glass bells were suspended from the ceiling with matching counterweights . . . when someone wanted to cut off some cheese, he slid the heavy cover up into the air and reached for a wide-bladed cheese knife.

. . . Can you remember?

A candy case stood up near the front, where light was better, and candy was arranged in dishes with scalloped edges. Chocolate nougats, chocolate creams, nut clusters, and those tiny odd-shaped candies of many colors which were used for decorating birthday cakes; and round sugary balls which looked like oversized mothballs . . . each of those had a filbert inside. Caramels, stick candy in jars, horehound sticks in jars . . . wee red cinnamon candies which were called *whisky-killers*, because they would take bad odors away from your breath and make it agreeable.

When you went with Mother or Grandmother to the store, when she paid her bill each month— After the bill was paid, the grocer would go around behind the candy counter. He'd take a small paper sack, striped in colors, and gather up an assortment of various candies: a large or a small assortment, depending on how generous the grocer felt at the moment, and depending also upon the size of the bill just paid. He'd award the candy free of charge, as a kind of bonus.

You liked to go with Grandmother or Mother when she paid her bill!

. . . And her meat bill at the butcher's, too. Because the butcher might gather up a ring of bologna, and wrap it, and hand it over as his form of bonus . . . not at all similar to those flat slices of bologna you buy in plastic envelopes nowadays. He made the bologna himself . . . it cost five or ten cents a ring.

. . . I think it was Mr. Bud Bossert who offered the first grapefruit for sale. They lay in a bushel basket up front, and were objects of curiosity to people who came from the more remote portions of our County. They stared at the grapefruit, asking in puzzlement, "What's them?"

Charley Lacey sped around town in a light wagon, keeping his brown horse at a trot most of the time. It was interesting to watch Charley driving and delivering, because he had but one arm. He'd stop at the Hughes' or the Quackenbushes' or the Teals', vault out of the wagon, reach back in the open box, pull out the basket of groceries, clamp it against his chest, and lug it to the kitchen door. There was no extra charge for this service. Downtown was a long way for older people to walk, and there were only three automobiles in town.

Back down on Main Street, telephones were jangling. Jennie or Will or Effie took more orders for the afternoon delivery. "Oh yes, Mrs. Whitley. . . . Five bars of Fels Naptha soap . . . yes. Two pounds of coffee . . . do you wish it ground? Oh no, I remember you prefer to grind your own . . . yes, one pound of lard . . . one sack Gold Medal flour . . . you want the full forty-nine-pound size? . . . Dark-brown sugar, two pounds. . . . Need any butter today? We've just opened a fresh tub."

Remember?

I doubt that you do, unless you're *very* gray.

Small-town factories were usually called "machine shops." Most of the products were tooled by hand.

People who worked in the factories walked to work. No one had ever seen a factory parking lot, no one envisioned such a thing.

No one had ever heard of a Laundromat. . . . Monday was wash day with its galvanized tubs, and boiler-on-the-stove, and water drawn from the cistern, and bluing poured in to keep the clothes white. And the long lines of wires out in the back yard, waiting for their burden . . . secret, significant, bifurcated garments were hung at the *far* end of the line, hidden behind flapping sheets, well away from eyes of the menfolks.

There wasn't a Stop sign in Hamilton County or any need for one. At railroad crossings they had wooden signs: LOOK OUT FOR THE CARS. Meaning railroad cars.

There wasn't a Pure sign or a Texaco sign or a Standard sign anywhere about.

There weren't any beer signs. There wasn't any beer. Hamilton County was dry.

The Mobil Chemical Industrial plant hadn't been constructed . . . meadowlarks owned the area. Grandpa Gebner was still alive. (Still alive? Thunderation!—he was forty-six years old.) Dewey and Leila had only been married a few years, and they were living in the old house too . . . the farm was a busy place. A minor tragedy befell the Gebners when lightning struck a chimney, and the chimney had to be rebuilt. Grandpa Gebner bought a set of lightning rods from the first salesman who came by.

. . . The Gebners' residence decays, with its brick spring-house alongside. That was a kind of creamery, with wide flat pans of milk sitting in the gloom, waiting for cream to rise.

Ah yes, the apple tree still blooms in spring . . . you can see blossoms on the roof. And also a shred of flowering shrubbery survives. Grandma Gebner set that out, seventy years ago.

. . . Lot of noise there at the Mobil Chemical Industrial plant.

Where have the larks gone?

275

*T*hat's quite a complex which has arisen next to the old grain elevator alongside the Northwestern tracks. The *Freeman–Journal* said that they were only thirty days away from planned completion of a new 420,000 bushel elevator being built eight miles up the line, at Woolstock. "John Rodenberg, manager of the Farmer's Co-operative Elevator Company which will have a 1,100,000 bushel storage capacity when the new facilities are completed, said today that the 10-silo structure is a $245,000 concrete reinforced steel addition to the Woolstock outlay. Features of the new elevator include areated storage which allows wet corn to be stored, and a heat detection unit to warn of possible danger of fire. Rodenberg said that the building will reach 130 feet from its base and is as wide as it is tall. Conveyor belts will link the new and older buildings, which include a 200,000 bushel elevator and a grain drier."

Well, if the *Freeman* is right about that, it's quite an enterprise. . . . Rather a far cry from the days when Adam McKinlay was manager of the old elevator at Woolstock, and Mr. Jacobs used to come driving up a wooden ramp with his team of Belgians hauling a lumber wagon filled to the brim with oats. Chocks would be put in place, and then Adam would operate a crank with its linked chain . . . the floor tilted, oats slid in a rich golden stream into the bin below.

You're apt to say, "I guess everything has changed." But you're wrong if you say and believe it. Because boys and girls still like to gather beside an open fire—or maybe stray into romantic darkness, away from that same fire.

Along comes a wedding . . . along comes a baby.

The old order changeth, whether in grocery stores or in pastures once made melodious by the larks . . . Grandma and Grandpa go their ordained ways.

But babies are an article eternal, whether in Hamilton County or any place else.

. . . Also they grow tall in time.